A
TELLING
OF
STONES

NEIL RACKHAM

A
TELLING
OF
STONES

ILLUSTRATED BY ALISDAIR WISEMAN

Contents

Foreword

List of Illustrations

12 The Drowned Princess
On the Nature of the Memory of Stones

20 Crossing Uig Sands
On the Nature of Seeing Stones

28 The Whirlpool at Lochlin
On the Nature of Foretelling with Stones

42 Twists in the Knot
On the Nature of Second Sight

52 The Stone Stirs in Lochlin
On the Nature of Celtic Knots

62 Of Malice and Poison
On the Nature of Twists in the Knot of Time

70 Prelude to a Raid
On the Nature of Stout Ships

78 The Stone at Loch Ussie
On the Nature of Ravens

86 The Two Pedlars
On the Nature of the Summer Walkers

100 A Rhyme, a Riddle and a Secret
On the Nature of the Blue Men of the Minch

114 The Dry Well
On the Nature of Wells

126 The Selkie from Lochlin
On the Nature of Selkies

142 The Stone at Brahan
On the Nature of Women with Red Hair

152 Of Carvers and Sagas
On the Nature of Walruses and their Ivory

168 Portents at Brahan

176 The Seer's Parting
On The Nature of the Penalties of Foretelling

196 The Return to Baile na Cille

Endnotes
On the Nature of the Team Behind the Book

Acknowledgements

Map

Foreword

Like living creatures, legends are shaped by the principle of survival of the fittest. If I tell you a story and it doesn't interest you, you won't retell it and so it becomes extinct then and there. For a tale to become a legend, handed down through many generations, it must survive by tapping into something deep and compelling. To be passed on it must be memorable; it has to spark curiosity and invite questions. It must earn the right to a retelling.

This is exactly the effect that a particular legend had on me one rainy lunch-time, as I sat in the Uig Community Centre cafe on the Isle of Lewis, reading an article in the local newsletter. It told of an island tale: a princess drowned in a pool below Baile na Cille, not a mile from where I was. Uig is an area on the wind-swept west coast of Lewis, remote and little visited by princesses. So that, in itself, caught my interest. What was she doing there? I read further. There was a storm and a shipwreck. I might have quickly forgotten the whole tale, except for two distinct details that kept my interest alive. Around her neck was a seeing stone. I was mystified because I hadn't a clue what a seeing stone was or why it might be significant. The second detail was even more intriguing. The seeing stone was destined to become the property of the Brahan Seer.

Had I gone to school in Scotland I would almost certainly have been taught about the Brahan Seer. He was the Nostradamus of Scotland, famed for his wide-ranging and extraordinary prophecies. There are many books and stories about his predictions and his grisly death. A few hours of research and some questions to local people gave me a fairly good understanding of the sparse details of his life that are generally agreed to be true. He was born in the Uig area to a mother who had an unusual capacity to see the future. At some point he moved to the mainland and worked on the Brahan estates of the aristocratic Seaforth family. He became famed for his prophecies, made with the help of a seeing stone. He predicted the downfall of the Seaforths and, for this, was accused of witchcraft. He was burned alive in a barrel of tar and didn't live to witness the decline of the Seaforths, which happened precisely as he had foreseen. Delving further, I met a tangle of contradictions. There was no agreement as to when the Seer lived; some accounts had him on the Isle of Skye two hundred years before he was supposedly born on Lewis. While there was general agreement that he used a seeing stone, there were widely different versions of how the stone came into his possession; the drowned princess being just one of many suggested routes.

As I read more deeply, the life of the Brahan Seer became an ever more tangled knot of possibilities. I decided to organise the many contradictory tales to see if I could unravel them into one fairly coherent account. To do this, the seeing stone was the key and that's where I began my more detailed investigations.

Seeing stones are stones that have one or more small natural holes through them. They have a long history. It's a matter of scientific fact that if you look through a small hole, you can see distance more clearly than with the naked eye. As physicists put it, by decreasing aperture you increase definition. In the days before spectacles or telescopes, stones with holes must have been important to a seafaring people who needed to scan the horizon for ships or landfalls. Perhaps that importance is why seeing stones have been found in so many prehistoric coastal burial sites. It's a small step for the imagination to believe that if a stone allows you to see the present more clearly, then perhaps it could also let you see into the future. And so the legends of fabled seeing stones began to be shared. These stones were said to have supernatural powers of divination, although they usually exacted a price from the user in the form of ill luck.

This book traces different versions of tales that are told about one powerful stone, variously called the Tostesson Stone, the Brahan Stone or the Lochlann Stone. I've used sources from the islands of Lewis and Harris, from the Isle of Skye, the Orkneys and the Shetlands as well as from the mainland of Scotland. I've incorporated elements of the tale from as far afield as Ireland, Norway and Iceland. Inevitably, like all tellers of folk tales, I've had to use my own inventions to fill in many of the gaps. Because one legend leads into others, I've learned about selkies, about the nature of wells, pedlars and ships, about the Blue Men of the Minch and the Lewis Chessmen. I've been drawn along by these and many other threads that make up the intricate tapestry of Hebridean lore and I've tried to weave some of this additional exploration into this book of tellings. If, like me, you find these stories compelling, I hope that you'll contribute to their survival by passing them on.

Neil Rackham
Edinburgh

List of Illustrations

12   The stone in the pool at Baile na Cille

20   A cart piled high with kelp

28   Breakan's Cave and Halldóra's Leap

42   The ruins of a stone shieling at the side of the loch

52   A pool where a peat-brown river frets at the edge
       of the sea

62   Kenneth Odhar's cottage

86   A pedlar's stone by the side of the water

100   Gallan Head and the jagged rocks of Uig

114   Baile na Cille graveyard at night

152   Lewis Chessmen

176   Shieling above Baile na Cille

The Drowned Princess

THIS TALE WOULD SEEM SIMPLE. It is of a princess drowned in the pool at Baile na Cille on the sands of Uig, where a peat-brown river frets at the edge of the sea. You would seem to know the end of the story before you know its beginning. Yet, like a Celtic knot, when its intricacies are traced there is no beginning, only twists and retellings that loop without ending.

The story is a compelling one: a drowned princess, here at the remotest rim of the world. Who was she? From where did she come? Explanations have evolved over centuries among the small communities that edge the northern seas. In some accounts, the princess is Norse, in some Irish. She is variously from Lochlin or from the Orkney Islands. While there is no agreement as to her identity or origin, or even to the events that brought her to her death, one curious detail is present in almost every telling of her tale. Around her neck she is said to wear a smooth stone, the size of a pebble. It is this stone, with its mystery and malice, that links all the events and versions that will be recounted here. The first of these, fittingly, comes from the Uig area on the west coast of Lewis.

An uneasy dawn broke over Uig, where folk were waking from a troubled night. The wind had screamed and cursed into the

wee hours, drowning out the savage crashing of the surf. During
the night, giant boulders were tossed as toys; whole sand dunes
disappeared and new ones grew from nothing. The ruins of ancient
buildings had been uncovered briefly and reburied. It had been
a night of fear. Parents had huddled their children to them and
the stones of the stoutest houses were shaken with a supernatural
violence. Then, about an hour before dawn, all became strangely
quiet and an exhausted sleep descended on the community.

In the steel light of dawn the body of a young woman lay in
a sheltered pool at Baile na Cille, on the edge of the sands, awaiting
discovery. She was the Princess Gradhag of Lochlin, a raider nation
that had long preyed on coastal settlements such as those around
Uig Bay. Her body moved gently with the waves that broke over the
rocks at the pool edge. Around her neck she wore a leather pouch
on an elaborate neckpiece plaited from leather strips which had
already turned sea-sodden and black. Her flaxen hair, more alive
than in life, streamed out in the current, wafting and eddying like
kelp to the waves, snaking her spirit away into the sea. The drowned
princess had dealt in prophecy, which is to know an end before
its time. But foretelling had always proved as treacherous as the
waters of the Minch. It was a defiance. It cut the knot to see what
was not meant to be seen. In consequence, prophecy often came at
a terrible price and so it had been with this princess.

People woke to cries and shouts. The sands and the rocks beyond
were strewn with the remains of a great raiding fleet from Lochlin.
Five fine ships lay smashed and splintered. Only two survivors were
found among nigh on a hundred men dead and drowned. As was
the custom, the settlements of the bay gathered all that could be
salvaged and sorted it into four piles on the sands; one pile for
wood, one for iron; one pile for weaponry, one for the woven matter
of ropes, sailcloth and clothing stripped from the dead.

It was some time before a child from Timsgarry came upon the
body of the Princess lying in the pool. When the adults arrived

they stared at the drowned figure, amazed at the fine garments she wore. It was a rare thing to see a drowned raider woman, for attacking from the sea was men's work. She stared up from beneath the water, her body rising and falling with each wave and her pale face blank amidst her rippling hair. For a long time, folk stared at her in silence, wondering who was this young woman, whose daughter could she be; whose wife? What omens and portents might her death mean? They gazed down at her fine clothes and asked each other what wheel could spin threads so delicate and yet so strong? What loom could weave so tight? What dyestuffs stain so brightly? The men were filled with a deep foreboding. They knew these clothes to be a forewarning. From them they could discern a formidable enemy with power and knowledge. A people weaving garments like these could make fast ships and sharp weapons. The men shuddered, anticipating war and ravages. The women were filled with wonder. The fine clothes unsettled them. They tried to imagine the soft feel of their fabric on the skin. As they whispered to each other, here in the presence of death, they were unable to suppress secret images of first their children and then themselves clad in such finery. But they also knew these clothes were sodden with ill luck and not for them.

Eventually, they reached down to pull her body from the pool. Kneeling beside her in the sand, a man from Carnish tugged on her plaited neckpiece. He cut open its leather pouch, hoping for jewels or gold. Inside lay a ring, a silver key with an intricately fashioned head and a pale pebble. He held the key up for all to see while he slipped the ring unnoticed into his pocket. Finally he looked at the pebble and, deciding it to be worthless, tossed it impatiently back into the water. Watched by his neighbours he examined every inch of the neckpiece and every fold of its pouch. He scoured every detail of the intricate plaitwork across his palm, but there were no more hidden riches, and much he was unable to tell. It had been crafted from the skin of a ewe, but not any ewe.

It had been tanned, but not as ordinary skins were tanned. Afterwards, in secret, the man studied the ring he had taken. It was a man's ring, with old runes engraved upon it and with a small irregular red jewel set into it, its shape resembling a seal. The man from Carnish knew that he had filched an item of great value, but he could not know that this salt-stained leather pouch had held something of still greater value: a seeing stone of immense power which his inadvertent hand had sent spiralling down to obscurity in the pool.

There it lay now, sleeping, dreaming or plotting until a rain of fibres, a drizzle of filaments, would one day waken it.

After the burials they will take her outer costume to Carnish where each piece will become a wonder for many years to come. For generations, wide-eyed children will stroke them threadbare. The women will tell tales around them, intricate as the weaving itself and just as richly embroidered.

In a future time, Coinneach Odhar, a man of Uig who will become famed throughout Scotland as the Seer of Brahan, will find the last remnant of the once-fine dress that adorned the Princess Gradhag in a chest belonging to his grandmother. Unbeknown to him, the Stone that graced the neck of the drowned princess will soon come into his own possession. He will be fated to pluck that very Stone from where it has lain so long on the pool bed at Baile na Cille. But for now, as he fingers the tattered cloth, he is innocent of what awaits him. His will be the final hand to touch these fragile threads. Thinking them to be worthless, he will consign them to the waves, seeking luck. On a rare still day he will carry them, with other broken remnants from his grandmother's life, to the cliffs above Mangersta, where the waves are ever restless. There he will toss his handful of fragments into the sea. A wind will spring from nowhere and catch the feathery wisps of the once-fine cloth, leaving shards of pottery and a worn leather thimble to tumble down into the waters. The threads will carry high over the hill, over Carnish, over the sands of Uig and fall like rain into the pool where a princess in another time has drowned, and where the Stone will lie waiting to be found. In this manner, one loop of the knot will be completed as another starts.

On the Nature of the Memory of Stones

The mountains of Lewis are the oldest in all the world and the boulders and stones from these mountains have long memories. The Black Nuns of Mealista chose to site their convent in the shelter of Mealaisbhal, the highest mountain in Lewis, whose great age infused each boulder with memory of a time when the world was at peace.

∞

All stones hold a remembrance of the past but Seeing Stones, or stones of vision, hold memories within them of things yet to come.

∞

If a man finds a rock that has been split in two from the force of a fall, he can win good luck by fitting the halves back together. This is because each half remembers its twin and grants luck as a reward for their reuniting.

∞

A pebble, large or small, has memory. Long into the night it will remember the heat of the day. The sound of the sea is retained deep within it.

∞

If blood is shed upon a stone, whether by war or through mishap, the stone remembers. Such stones may not safely be used for building as they will shudder at full moon on midwinter nights and the building will fall. After the bloody battle of Myrwodin, the battlefield land was granted to a knight who had fought well for victory. To keep wolves from his sheep, he built a mighty stone pen. Unknowingly, his masons used stone from the battlefield. The blood had long washed away but its remembrance remained. On the night of St Lucie, being close to the longest night of the year, there was also a full moon. The pen shuddered and fell in upon itself and all the sheep died.

∞

A house where folk have long sung and chattered, and where children have played, will be a happy house always, because the stones of the house will remember and ever resonate with good sounds.

∞

Lodestones bear a memory of the north from whence they came. It is told that an ice giant was enraged in consequence of an insult to his kind made by a raven that flew off to the south. In his rage, which lasted forty years, the ice giant flung thousands upon thousands of lodestones after the raven, hoping that one might strike. The stones landed many hundreds of leagues from their northlands home. The pangs within them, resulting from their separation, were so full of pain that they were felt by the gods, who transformed the giant himself into stone, that he might understand the hurt he had caused. Over many ages, he lost all mortal shape and became the great mountain of Galdhøpiggen. But the pangs remain to this day in the memory of the stones he flung, which is why a lodestone suspended from a string will still point to its northern home.

∞

Chieftain Stones, sometimes called Clan Stones or Sacred Stones, hold a memory of clan succession and are employed in the confirmation of each new clan chief. The people of Uig had a Clan Stone with a footprint embedded in it. Each new clan leader placed his foot in this indentation and swore to follow in the footsteps of earlier chiefs. To save the Uig Stone from raiders, Angus, the ruler of all the Long Island, had the Uig Stone locked in Rodel church, being the principal church of Harris. The men of Uig were unhappy with Angus for his neglect of them and stole the Stone from Rodel Church, intending to choose a new chief of their own. The Stone was heavy and it took them some days to carry it back across the mountains to Uig. Angus, forewarned of their deed, set out from Harris by sea and awaited them on the sands of Uig Bay with a large party of armed men. In the ensuing battle, the Uig Stone vanished and has not been seen since. Some say it disappeared of its own accord, being unwilling to hold the memory of this shameful incident. A tale was told that it was found again one hundred years later by Roderick MacKenzie of Uig. This story lacks credence because he described the stone he discovered as indented with a left foot, while the Uig Stone had a clear impression of a right foot embedded in it.

Crossing Uig Sands

I T IS NOT THAT THE SEEING STONE LIED. It saw a truth, or part of a truth. But truth has many strands that weave together like the most intricate of Celtic knots. And like these knots, there are points where the many filaments of a truth cross, only to loop around, disappear or reappear unexpectedly. Legends arise in countless versions because truth is infinitely varied. The Stone saw one thread of this, but where that thread would lead was obscure. There are points of inflection where the threads of time converge and at those points the many appearances of truth are united. Such a pivotal point is the pool on the sands of Uig Bay below Baile na Cille, whose waters change with the tide.

The Seeing Stone lay in the pool at Baile na Cille, where a peat-brown river fretted at the edge of the sea. The Stone had lain here, unseen and untouched, for centuries since it was taken from the neck of a drowned princess. It had great power. In the future, men would think it malevolent because it foresaw death. Yet to hold such a belief would be to mistake the nature of stones. The Stone was drawn to this pool because here was the point where many truths crossed; where many confused *seeings* became clear. It foresaw a tragic happening here. It may not have foreseen its own destiny. So now it lay, half buried in sand and

21

resting among simple pebbles that lacked its power. As to how it came there, we know one strand: a princess who wore it was drowned in this place. Other strands of the same tale have the Stone captured for a while by the Blue Men of the Minch and moving along alternative paths before blending by fate into the pebbles on the sands of Uig Bay.

At length the Stone left this pool and, through the interaction of many possibilities, passed into the hands of Kenneth Odhar, the great Seer of Brahan.[1] Let us grasp one strand of its leaving and follow it.

It was a July day. The sands of Uig Bay shimmered in the hot, still afternoon. Three young men had come down from Carnish, pushing a cart piled high with kelp. They were making their way to the lazy-beds below Timsgarry. There they would turn the kelp and churn it for months until the rain washed all trace of the sea from it. Then they would carry it to the runrigs and mix the kelp with peat and make it ready for next year's plantings. It was hard labour, but that was the lot of these three young men and it was their expectation. They had not, however, anticipated this unaccustomed July heat. Today the air was unnaturally motionless, as if the whole island waited. The tide was out and the pale sands of the bay were vast. The heat reflected onto the faces of the three men from Carnish; they sweated much and they were thirsty. Perhaps it was their thirst, perhaps some other force, which drew them away from the direct route across the sand. A slight diversion to the left brought them to the pool at Baile na Cille, where the water was drinkable on the ebb tide, though slightly brackish.

Iain, the oldest of the three, was a large man, standing a full head above the others. His father was a blacksmith, as was his grandfather, and in due time he would take over the forge at Timsgarry himself. Today, despite his great strength, exertion in the unusual heat had exhausted him. He fell to his knees with a great sigh and drank deeply from the stream where it entered the pool. The others followed, cupping the cool water that was darkened and smoky with peat, feeling contentment in each deep swallow. Soon, as young men will, they revived and before long they were jumping into the pool, shouting and splashing, with their hours of toil forgotten. They plucked pebbles from the bottom of the pool and threw them with all their might down along the curve of the wide stream where it flowed at the edge of the sands. Young Kenneth Odhar had a strong arm but he was no match for his companions. He sensed that the other two were turning this into a contest. Having no inclination to be shown weak, he left the pool and splashed downstream, saying he would act as judge to see which of his friends threw the furthest. To entice them to cast beyond the limits of their earlier efforts he walked further and further out onto the sand until he was impossibly distant from them. In this way, as the weakest of the three, he made gentle mockery of his stronger friends.

For his last throw, Iain Macaulay reached to the depths of the pool until his hand touched upon a smooth stone half buried in the sand. He was never to know that this was no ordinary pebble: it had spent an age waiting for this moment. It glistened in the sunlight as he rubbed it clean. It had a hole through it, remarkable for its exact circularity. The stone was pale, almost white, and fitted the hand as if made to be held. Macaulay thought nothing of these things and swung his arm to make a final cast. He timed his release poorly, yet the stone soared high, twisting in the air like a gull in flight; as if possessed of wings. It travelled more than twice the distance of any previous throw, heading straight towards Kenneth Odhar, who was forced to jump from its path. All three young men were struck silent for a moment by the extraordinary feat. Then, while the other two shouted and splashed, Kenneth walked to the stone and picked it up. For a moment he considered throwing it back towards the pool. Then he saw that the stone was remarkable. It curved itself to his hand and, as he grasped it, he sensed strangeness: it tingled. He saw the faint rune-like marking on its whitish surface. The hole through the stone was not in its centre, yet it was perfect. He raised it towards his good right eye to look through it but found that the stone or his hand – he could not tell which – drew the hole instead to his left eye, which from childhood had been weak.

When the pebble came level with his left eye, he was amazed. He could see clearly through it. He tested this again. He took the stone away and, closing his right eye, looked back at his friends in the pool. He saw two blurred figures but could not distinguish which was which. Bringing the stone to his eye again he now saw them with such unnatural clarity that he almost dropped it. Until this moment in his life, Odhar's nature had not been secretive. At any other time, with any other stone, he would have rushed back to his friends to share with them the excitement of discovery. But this stone was already changing young Kenneth Odhar and he slipped it into his pocket, saying nothing on his return.

The three young men, their strength renewed, took up the kelp cart once more and pushed on towards Timsgarry. The others thought little of the silence that had come over Kenneth, for he was ever inclined to be of a quiet nature. As they moved out again across the sands of Uig Bay they joked and boasted, and the cart turned and twisted as their attention drifted from their course. The wheels of the cart traced drunken twin strands in the sand behind them, much like intertwining threads of kelp in the fierce currents off Gallan Head. Two old crofters, looking down on this scene from the hills above, smiled and shook their heads at the wasted energy of youth. The Stone was moving along these twisted threads and, after many motionless years, it was ready to weave its way towards destinies that none might guess.

On the Nature of Seeing Stones

Any stone that has through its body a natural hole of sufficient width to allow clear sight is a seeing stone. If the hole is made by man, or if it has been artificially enlarged, the stone will not see. But, while all natural seeing stones have some sight, albeit limited, only a choice few of their number can see forward through the mists of time.

∞

A true seeing stone shows the future but, because the future is not meant to be seen, its divination may prove inexact. First, the stone may see a future that will never take place. Second, it may see only part of a future, omitting some detail of grave significance. Because of this, stones are often perceived to be malevolent or to have a treachery within them.

∞

Some say that truth lies only at the edge of perception. So the most exact seeing requires glimpsing the periphery of the stone's apparition using the corner of the eye.

∞

The foresight of a seeing stone is at its most exact in the hour after dawn. It is thought by many that this may be more a consequence of the freshness of the eye than of the power of the stone. A tired eye may see strangely.

Seven MacLeods from Kishorn ventured onto MacKenzie land to recover sheep that had strayed. On their return, having chased deeper afield than they had planned, evening was upon them, leaving them apprehensive and weary. In this reduced state, their leader James, a seer of some considerable reputation, put his stone to his eye fearing an ambush might await them.

The stone revealed to him that scores of armed MacKenzies were in wait two miles ahead where the glen narrowed. He saw with great clarity how he and his friends would die in the skirmish. Despite his most dire warnings, the other six decided to press on with the sheep, there being no other easy way home. James, declaring this foolhardy, refused to join them and made a detour upwards of twenty miles. Many hours later he reached Kishorn with a heavy heart, fearing his friends dead, only to learn that they had returned in safety having seen not one sign of MacKenzies. Thereafter, none had regard for his foresights, all as a happenstance of looking through a weary eye.

∞

A seer with a blind eye sees truest. This is because a good eye sees the present and may inadvertently introduce that which is current into that which is yet to be. This distraction may make the foretelling less exact. In some accounts Kenneth Odhar, the Brahan Seer, had a blind eye and, in consequence, saw the better for it.

∞

Seeing stones are of the sea and become weak if removed from their home. To retain its strength a stone must be brought within the sound of the sea and, if it has been long away, it must be immersed in the waves below the spring tide point for three days and three nights. The Hermit of Schiehallion had a seeing stone. He dwelt on the magic mountain for forty years, far distant from the sea's song. His wisdom was great and many came from the coast to consult with him. In exchange for his advice he required these visitors to bring him a gill of seawater. In this way he renewed the life of his stone. He kept the stone within a large shell where the sound of the sea, though faint, sustained it also.

∞

Stones with the best promise of seeing will be discovered along a beach that faces west. The stone will be found above the low mark of a spring tide and below the high mark of a neap tide. The more perfect the circularity of its hole, the clearer will be the seeing. But it must be added that the Stone of Mull has a hole of an irregular shape which has not disadvantaged its power.

∞

A seeing stone, if it is found within a well, may have extraordinary power. Wizards are said to hide the strongest stones there to prevent discovery by their rivals, for, by divination and second sight, the presence of a stone can be sensed from far off. But when immersed in a deep well, the stone is all but impossible to discern.

∞

Sailors may employ seeing stones to navigate through fog and mist. A raiding fleet from the north trapped Allain of the clan MacFie, in the sea loch at Sunart,

intending to capture or kill him. The raiders waited at the mouth of the loch, their ships in a blockade, confident that their quarry had no escape. They knew nothing of the penetrating power of stones. A heavy sea fog descended over them, in the thick of which Allain, using a simple stone plucked that day from the beach, was able to see their position and slip between them unnoticed.

∞

Selkies use such stones to see clearly underwater. The Blue Men of the Minch have a powerful seeing stone that senses ships from far off.

∞

Some say that good stones may be found in the nests of ravens.

∞

It has been much argued as to whether the gift of seeing lies within the stone or within its user. The Hermit of Schiehallion was of the opinion that the gift lies in the user and that all but the strongest stones are no more than a lens to magnify the gift. It is well known that second sight passes most often through the female line, giving weight to the supposition that a stone alone is not sufficient for seeing but requires a user who has inherited second sight.

The Whirlpool of Lochlin

THE PRINCESS GRADHAG, whose sodden body was to be lifted from the pool at Baile na Cille, was not the first of her bloodline to be entangled in the twisting snare of the Stone. Many generations before her the Stone had changed the fate of another princess of Lochlin.

It was in the era of the Old Kingdom, at the time when Lochlin had lately risen from the sea. The youthful Princess Halldóra, now in her sixteenth year, was playing with her two younger sisters in their father's hall when she came upon a small box made of rare yew wood, tucked beneath the great chair the King used when greeting visitors of distinction. Opening the box, she found within it a strangely marked pale stone with a hole. It fitted easily to her hand.² On holding it to her eye the startled girl saw, distinctly, a young man, clearly a nobleman, and heard him speak: "I, Breakan, Prince of Norway, son of Jørgen Oddmundsen, descendant of the great Jarl Skule Tostesson, am drawn to visit you."

Halldóra dropped the Stone and looked in alarm around her father's hall, but the place was empty. After a while her trembling subsided and she dared to pick it up again. She was about to raise it once more to her eye when she heard footsteps. Hastily she replaced the Stone within its yew box and stood in time to greet

29

her father the King, who entered with two men. These men were emissaries from Norway and the Princess, knowing her manners, bobbed politely, sent her sisters to their nurse and removed herself to a small chair at the side of the hall. There she listened, her heart still thudding, while the men in their thick accents spoke with her father of alliances. She had little interest in the talk of men; her mind was still taken up by the mysterious image and the voice of the young man in the Stone. Suddenly she heard his name again, this time on the lips of her father: 'Breakan'. From that moment she listened intently, though feigning the discreet indifference that was seemly in a young princess. Prince Breakan would visit them next year. He was young and eligible. A union would be possible.

The months passed and Halldóra found herself dreaming of the unknown Prince, imagining a life of happiness with him. She hardly knew how to account for these dreams, even to herself. Many times she was tempted to use the Stone to confirm her hopes, but she sensed, dimly, that she had done wrong in finding and using it and she dreaded that it might punish her by showing her something she would not want to see. Curiosity in the young has always been stronger than caution, however, and so it was that one day Halldóra crept again into her father's hall and reached for the box beneath his great chair. Shaking, she held the Stone to her eye and there, just as clearly, she saw him. Prince Breakan was speaking once more, but this time not to her. Halldóra watched, her heart in turmoil, as she realized what the Stone was showing her. Breakan was parting from a weeping girl with long flaxen hair. Again she heard his voice. "All is done between us, Ansfrida. My father has chosen me a bride in Lochlin and I dream of her."

Much comforted, Halldóra replaced the Stone and went from the hall into the bright spring afternoon. Yet it is in the nature of women to plague themselves with doubt, and the next day she returned to her father's chair hoping for yet more reassurance. Again she raised the Stone and this time she saw her rival, Ansfrida, lying dead of grief. With her rival gone the Princess felt a surge of confidence, but by now her appetite for the Stone's good tidings had become a compulsion and on the next day she knew she must make another seeing. Once again she quietly entered the hall and reached for the box. It had gone.

Halldóra's initial panic at the removal of the yew box became a quiet frenzy as she realised over time that it had been removed *from her.* For weeks she searched without giving the appearance of seeking. She looked for her sister's lost ball behind the coils of rope in the old store barn; she visited the weaponry forge, feigning an interest in the armourer's craft while she poked into possible hiding places among the piles of frayed banners and pennants ranged along the wall. But the old yew box was not to be found, so she could only wait impatiently as the summer approached, and with it the visit of the Prince himself. During these weeks Halldóra engaged her father the King in discourse about Norway. She was alarmed to find that he had many doubts about Breakan and his family.

"My father had skirmishes with his father, Jørgen Oddmundsen," he told her. "In those times his family was great. It is told that their fortune came from sorcery and from using a seeing stone that had guided them since the days of Jarl Skule Tostesson. In one such skirmish, your grandfather took the Stone from him and, since then, their house has been in decline."

"What became of the Stone, Father?"

"When I received it from my own father I looked through it many times and saw nothing. Mayhap its power is gone. For many years it has lain beneath my great chair but, acting upon a dream, I have moved it for safekeeping to my bedchamber."

The day came when the long waiting was at an end and Prince Breakan arrived in a fine ship. It was stoutly made and it drew

31

the admiration of all Lochlin, where the shipwright's trade was held in high esteem. Halldóra, standing nervous and pale beside her father on the quay, experienced a shock of recognition as she watched Breakan disembark. The Stone had told her true. The Prince was in every way just as she had seen and heard him. For his part, the Prince seemed much taken with Halldóra and over the following hours the two exchanged glances of unmistakable meaning. The Princess assumed her role of diligent hostess with modesty and waited for the men to decide her future. She longed for the reassurance of the Stone but did not dare to try and find it.

On the seventh day of the royal visit the Prince asked Halldóra's father for her hand. The King hesitated but promised an answer at the end of a further seven days. He summoned Halldóra.

"I gravely doubt his earnestness," he told her, "I must test him in some way."

Halldóra was terrified. Her heart was full of Breakan. She feared that the King would set some impossible task which her new love would fail to complete. She knew that the test must be difficult in order to satisfy her father but, for her to achieve her own desires, it must also allow the Prince to succeed. Searching in her mind for such a challenge, she thought at once of the Stone and knew it would guide her, reasoning that it saw for her and not for her father because it favoured her. She did not understand that seeing is most usually passed through the female line and that her own skill was from her mother, not from her father.

The next day the King went to the harbour to inspect the Prince's fine ship. While her father was away Halldóra entered his bedchamber and searched until she found the yew box. Her heart thudding, she removed the Stone. Looking through it she saw her love's ship riding the treacherous whirlpool of Lochlin, anchored by three stout cables. She could discern that each cable was woven and plaited from a different material. The first was made from fine wool, the second from the strongest hemp and the third from the braided hair of many maidens. Immediately she understood that this was the test Breakan would pass to win her hand.

When her father returned, Halldóra asked him whether he had yet determined on a test of sufficient challenge for the visiting Prince. The King replied that he was still considering the matter. Gathering up all her determination, the Princess proposed that securing a firm anchorage within the notorious whirlpool of Lochlin would be a suitable task, as it would require much courage, skill and purpose. Everyone knew the terrible ferocity of the waters there. The King was greatly taken with the notion, for he saw in it a test that the Prince could only fail yet, because it was Halldóra's own suggestion, he himself could not then be blamed for the failure. He summoned the Prince and agreed to give his daughter's hand in marriage if Breakan would anchor within the whirlpool of Lochlin for three days and three nights. At first the young Prince hesitated, but Halldóra drew him aside and whispered to him of the three stout cables and foretold with calm assurance that his success was certain. As a token of her love and reassurance, she gave him a ring that had been in her family for many years. It was a man's ring with old runes engraved upon it and, set into it, a small irregular red jewel, its outline resembling the shape of a seal. She slipped it upon his finger. It fitted perfectly.

"This is a good omen," she whispered, "and it tells us that if you take this challenge, you shall return safely"

Breakan accepted the challenge and agreed to enter the whirlpool on midsummer night of the next year. After a tender farewell between the young couple he returned to Norway and there he ordered three cables to be woven. Following Halldóra's precise instructions, the first cable he had made from the wool of rams from the Faroe Islands, the strongest wool in all the world. For the second cable he brought hemp from Ireland, famous for its ability to endure, grown on the fertile Shannon plains. For the final cable he sent his men to collect hair from the purest maidens of Norway. Such was the esteem in which Prince Breakan was held that this was gladly given. Even his erstwhile love, Ansfrida, shaved her head for him. For months the finest rope-makers wove stout cables of immense strength. Though the cable of maiden's hair was the thinnest, the innocence, goodwill and purity of the Norwegian women imparted to it a magical strength and Breakan felt complete certainty in the success of his venture. Finally, the cables were safely stowed in his stout ship and he set forth again for Lochlin.

On midsummer night the Prince's vessel entered the whirlpool and cast its three strong anchors, each held by a cable. The first day passed with ease. The whirlpool hissed around the ship but could not shake it. Then, in the dark of the night, a terrible wind sprang up from nowhere. Battered by the force of the gale, the woollen cable unravelled until, with a dreadful rending, it parted. The Prince and his crew stared into the whirling water in terror, but the two other cables held fast. The wind died down and the second day passed calmly. That night there rose a fierce swell and giant waves tossed the ship. In the morning the Prince and his crew found to their extreme dismay that the hemp cable had given way. They were now held only by the slender cable of maidens' hair. But on the third night the sea was quiet and the wind calm. Thinking the ordeal soon over, the crew was lulled to anticipation of success as Prince Breakan's ship rode the twisting waters of the whirlpool like a gull on the waves. They congratulated each other and blessed the purity of the Norwegian girls whose innocence had given a magical invulnerability to the last of their cables.

Then, in the dark moment before dawn, the cable split. The ship spun and was sucked beneath the swirling water. In minutes all were lost, except for one seaman and the Prince's dog. Breakan's shattered body was washed ashore and, such was the violence of the whirlpool, his remains could only be identified by the seal ring that Halldóra had given him. He was buried without ceremony in a cave that to this day is called Breakan's Cave or, by some, the Cave of the Prince. When the sole surviving seaman returned to Norway with tidings of the loss there was great sadness among the people. Ansfrida was overcome with grief and shame because, from her dalliances with Breakan, her hair had lost its purity and she knew that it was because of her that the cable was weakened. She would neither eat nor drink and, after three days and three nights, again at the dark moment before dawn, she died of her grief.

In Lochlin, Princess Halldóra awaited her love's return. A royal servant came with a report of a drowned man and brought with him the red seal ring that had been found on his finger. When Halldóra saw the ring she was dumb with anguish and disbelief. How could this have happened when the Stone had shown her so clearly what was to be? As in a trance she went to her father's bedchamber and took it from its yew box, thinking to destroy it for its treachery. Raising it for a last time to her eye she saw a princess lying drowned in a pool, her fair hair streaming out in the current, wafting and eddying like kelp to the waves. Believing this to be a foretelling of the manner of her own death, she dropped the Stone to the floor, her hands sweating. In the midst of her grief, a defiance rose within her. She would show the Stone it was wrong; she refused to drown as the Stone had foretold. The manner of her death would be of her own choosing, and in this small, despairing way Halldóra would defy the treacherous Stone. With her mind thus fortified, and before her courage could leave her, the Princess ran to the edge of the cliff, above the place that would one day become known as Breakan's Cave, and leapt out to her death on the rocks below. The sky darkened and there was a single fearsome clap of thunder which shook the entire island of Lochlin. A huge wave smashed into the cliff and, with its retreating roar, engulfed and carried away the broken body of Princess Halldóra.

At the moment of his daughter's leap, the King was entering his bedchamber. There was the Stone lying on the floor. He picked it up and raised it, without thinking, to his eye, but, because he had not the sight, he saw nothing. Then came the mighty peal of thunder and the King, dropping the Stone, rushed from the room, knowing suddenly that something of great consequence was amiss.

Later that evening, when the Princess Halldóra had failed to return, her father ordered a search to be made but it was dark and nothing was found. The searchers gathered again at daybreak and the King summoned his seer to guide them. The seer was aghast to learn from one of the King's valets that Halldóra had been seen creeping into her father's bedchamber to use his seeing stone. He asked for it and, when it was fetched, took it from its yew box and examined it closely. He realised immediately that this Stone had great power and might be malicious. He warned the King that ill might have befallen his daughter as a result of her untrained use of it, and predicted that there was little hope of finding the Princess unless the Stone was first made safe through spells. To render it harmless, he made a neckpiece from strips of plaited ewe leather and, with a heated dagger tip, burned into each strip the ancient runes that ward off evil influence. To these runes he added the name of Jarl Skule Tostesson, for he was the first known owner of the Seeing Stone and the use of his name gave dominion over its power. The seer plaited the ewe leather in a loop through the Stone's eye, so that the seeing hole was entirely blocked. In this way, no evil could pass through from the future to bring to the present any adverse luck that might impede the safe return of Princess Halldóra. As a final safeguard, he wove silver fishhooks into the fabric of the plait, that any remaining malice might be ensnared upon them. The searchers, meanwhile, combed the length and breadth of Lochlin. There was no fishing for three days while every boat, large and small, was ordered to scour each inlet and every bay around the island. Despite all efforts, the remains of the Princess were never found and there was talk among the common folk that her body had been sucked into the great whirlpool of Lochlin.

The King mourned Halldóra for a month and a day. As was the custom with a sudden death, when the time of mourning was done, he ordered the gathering together of his daughter's personal ornaments, intending to consign them to the sea. In the fulfillment of this custom he would forgive the sea for the taking of his daughter and the sea would, in turn, forgive any wrongs done to it by the King or his line. A servant collected up and brought him Halldóra's jewellery. There was the red seal ring. The King, fearing that it was tainted by ill luck, placed it in the yew box that had held the Stone, for yew is a protection against malice. He then examined her other jewels. There were six necklets he recognised and one he did not. He held it up to the light and saw that it was a necklace of barbed silver and leather decorated with runes, realising as he did so that this was the Seeing Stone itself, hanging from the plait that the seer had made. The grieving King hesitated. Then he read the name Jarl Skule Tostesson, burned into the leather. Uttering a curse of riddance upon the Jarl and all his line, he took the necklet and added it to his daughter's effects.

Climbing the cliff to the rock above the cave, he cast the ornaments one by one into the sea. His action aroused the curiosity of eight grey seals on the rocks below him and they raised their heads, craning their sleek necks in wonderment at the sight of a king casting jewels into the waves. Finally, only the Seeing Stone remained and, with a shout of rage, the King swung it upon its plait and hurled it from him. The necklace soared high and turned in the air like a gull in flight. It curved back towards the land; falling to the very rocks where the seals lay and, as if purposed, the barbed leather looped around the neck of the smallest of them. The seal shook and twisted its neck in panic, but the silver fishhooks bit into its skin and the necklet was soon tighter than any collar. The seal gazed towards the King and uttered a long, sad cry, as a child might when torn from its parents. Then it plunged into the waves, carrying away with it the Stone of Lochlin.

On the Nature of Foretelling with Stones

Although the future may be foretold by the casting of runes, by auguries or by the pattern of birds, there is no surer method than the use of a seeing stone.

∞

The talent to foretell with stones passes on the mother's side, although more men than women are numbered among the great seers.

∞

Stones foretell by vision but they can also foretell by voices that may be audible if the hole in the stone is held next to the ear. A woman's voice is sometimes heard, tempting with treacherous promises. Alistair MacBeth of Islay inherited a stone of considerable strength. On the night of a full moon he held it to his ear and heard a woman's voice of such charm and enchantment that he was powerless to resist it. Following its instructions he walked into the sea ever deeper until he was drowned, the stone sinking with him. Thus the Great Stone of Islay freed itself from mortal ownership.

∞

If a stone has been used by a person of malice, or by a wizard of evil intent, it becomes sullied. This may be cured through alternation of fire and ice. On the coldest of winter nights a fire must be kindled. The stone should then be placed in the fire until it emits a faint cry. Then it must be plucked from the fire and packed in ice or snow. If this is performed three times, the malice will be removed. It is widely believed that there are more sullied stones in the southern regions than in the north due to a lack of ice for this ritual cleansing.

∞

Many tales of seeing relate unfortunate events, telling of drownings or of death. In this way, the foretelling may appear to be sinister or even to be edged with malice. But this appearance is because dire consequences fasten forever within the memory, while happy outcomes often are forgotten or lie unrecorded. Calum Ferguson of Mull had a stone through which he could see only fortunate events. He correctly foresaw happy marriages, good fishing and excellent crops. The people of Mull believed that the stone itself brought this good luck, not apprehending that the stone could see only one side of fortune. The stone's fame drew many to Mull. And many returned empty handed when the stone saw nothing, not understanding that this result was of itself an ill omen.

∞

Foretelling needs a quiet heart free from wrong thoughts, because second sight is changed by the feelings of the seer. Women particularly may deform their vision through envy or jealousy; men through ambition or greed.

∞

Olaf the Wise was famed as the greatest prognosticator in all the world through the casting of runes, yet he failed to

see his own death. His nephew, looking
through a seeing stone that had
belonged to Birka of Björkö, saw his
uncle, drenched in blood, killed by an
arrow during a seal hunt. He sped to his
uncle to warn him of this dire event,
whereupon Olaf cast runes to verify
the lad's warning. The runes revealed
that he would, indeed, be invited to
participate in a seal hunt the next day
but that he would return unharmed.
In consequence, he dismissed the young
man's warning, joking with him that
in a contest between an inexperienced
lad with a stone of indifferent power
and the infallible rune-casts of Olaf the
Wise, there could only be one victor.
The following day he joined the hunt
and was struck in the neck by an arrow
that severed an artery, causing him to
bleed to death.

∞

A stone will see best when immersed
in the sea for an hour before it is put
to the eye, but, if a full soaking is not
a practical proposition, even the most
sparing sprinkling of seawater can be
beneficial for the accuracy of its seeing.
Some say that rubbing a seeing stone
with salt can efficaciously substitute
for the sea, although the evidence in
support of this is unreliable.

Twists in the Knot

I T IS CURIOUS THAT although we know much about the life and deeds of the mother of Kenneth Odhar, the Brahan Seer, we do not know her true birth name. Accounts of the time speak of her as the 'wise woman of Baile na Cille' and sometimes as *bean dubh,* which means 'the black woman'. This absence of a name was the more curious as the families of Uig are proud and have valued their lineage. In those days, even the name of a seventh child of a poor Uig crofter lost in infancy was recorded. From this, we may correctly infer that either the mother of the Seer chose to keep her true name a secret, or that others later expunged it from the records in the hope of expurgating the bad luck they supposed might reside in the very words of her name. It is therefore likely that she was a witch or, at the least, one who dabbled in the black arts. She will have known well that to give knowledge of her true name was to give others power over her. The name Odhar is from the Gaelic, meaning 'of a brown or sallow colour'. The Seer himself went under several names, such as Coinneach MacKenzie and Kenneth Seaforth. It has been suggested that his mother's name was known but remained unwritten through superstition of ill befalling those who wrote it. Certainly, the people of Uig were fearful of the ill-luck of naming.[3]

It has been said by some that the Seer's mother was Margaret Crowder, whose name appears written as Owder in the annals of the Black Nuns of Mealista. This is uncertain, but it is in the nature of stories of the Stone for much to be uncertain and Margaret Crowder shall be her name within this loop of its tale. Of the many accounts of how the Stone came to leave the pool at Baile na Cille this is the best known and is still today told throughout the land. This twist in the knot of the Stone is more readily traced than others and it is a matter of judgment whether it is the truer as a consequence of its familiarity.

Margaret Crowder tended cattle and goats in the hills around Timsgarry. She was possessed of *traibhse,* which is the second sight, enabling her to foresee events prior to their happening. Even among the crofters and sheep tenders of the Hebrides, whose second sight is known to be the strongest in all the world, she was famed. The people of Uig regarded her with an undisguised melding of admiration and fear. As a young girl she had foretold a drowning. Walking one day with her aunt along the road to Breanish, they met three boys. Margaret looked in fear at the eldest of the three and asked her aunt, "Why does he drip so wet? Why is he so pale? Why is his hair tangled and knotted with kelp?" The boys laughed, for the weather was dry and all were in the best of health. Next day, while fishing, the eldest boy caught his foot in a net and was dragged overboard and drowned. They pulled his body from the sea and at first could not recognize him, for his face was covered by a mass of kelp entangled with his hair.

As she grew, Margaret was observed to converse with herself as if she imagined a companion always at her side. There was talk that she saw a *fetch,* a likeness of oneself that appears to and advises those in whom the second sight is strongest. She often stared intently at nothing, her eyes following things others could not see. She made folk uneasy, so she was not invited to the *waulkings*, where women sat together to shrink and soften the new cloth. Instead she spent her days tending her goats. Notwithstanding the unease with which some regarded her, Margaret was a comely girl and the young men sought her company. She was espoused to a man from Mangersta, who himself had some second sight, and they were happy together until one night in a dream she saw her lover die in a quarrel in which his enemy struck him on the head with a heavy stone. Margaret woke in fear and her lover sprang up at the same moment, telling her that he had dreamed of his death at the hand of a Macaulay, where there had been bad blood for many generations. They agreed that fate might be forestalled if he fled south to Harris, where he had a sister who could offer him shelter. Accordingly, he left and for some weeks, hearing nothing, Margaret at first believed that fate had indeed been cheated by their act. But, as the days and long nights dragged on, she became apprehensive. She heard voices of doom in the wind. One night, when she went to *smor* her fire, tamping the peats around it to protect its heat, she stumbled with the ritual chanting that she had used since she was a child and the familiar words failed her for the first time. Even her second sight seemed to have abandoned her; her fetch kept away and refused to answer her summons. Finally, a black raven appeared at her chimney hole and Margaret knew in her heart that she would never again see the father of her bairn.

Then word came that her man's body had been found at Loch Scourst in the north of Harris. It seemed that on the first night of his journey he had sheltered in the ruins of a stone shieling at the side of the loch. In the wee hours a great wind blew up and loosened a large stone at the top of the shieling wall, which, falling upon the head of the sleeping man, had killed him instantly. The shieling had been built by Angus Macaulay of Maraig. In this way, the lovers' dreams proved unhappily true, which some took as a showing that while fate might in small degree be diverted, it could never be prevented in its entirety.

Left sorrowing, with no company but her young son Kenneth, Margaret received a visitation from her fetch, which tried to comfort her, offering news that Kenneth would one day become a great prophet. Margaret tried hard to pursue it on this matter but almost immediately the fetch fell silent. As if offended by her persistent questioning, the apparition deserted her then for seven nights and seven days. Then, on the eighth night it visited again but stood with its back to her. She saw that it held something up to its face but she could not discern what it was. The same thing happened upon the next night and on the next. In vain Margaret tried to walk around the spirit but it moved with her and she could see nothing but its back. On the fourth night, in desperation, she left her mirror at an angle to the wall, hoping to see a reflection of what the apparition carried but this also failed, for it is in the nature of a fetch to cast neither shadow nor reflection.

For the next two nights, Margaret tried to coax the fetch by pretending disinterest but still it turned its back on her and continued to raise the mysterious object to its face. Finally, instead of retiring to bed, Margaret took off her dress and put it once again upon herself, but backwards. The trick worked and the fetch appeared facing her. She could discern then that it had been holding up a blue stone, within which she could make out a hole of perfect circularity.[4] Margaret was intrigued and anxious. Now the spirit told her that this was none other than the celebrated Seeing Stone of Uig, which her son would one day employ to make prophecies that would be famed throughout Scotland and indeed for all time. Margaret would have to obtain it for her son through an act of courage in which she must hold a princess to ransom. The fetch then gave this dire warning: "Do not yourself look through the stone for, if you do so, you will die within the month. It is destined only for the eye of your son."

46

Years passed and although the apparition appeared many times to warn her of storms, of cattle poisonings and, more often, of events of a mundane nature, it never referred again to the Stone. Margaret half forgot what the fetch had foretold. Then, when Kenneth was in his fifteenth year, on the night of Hallowe'en, Margaret took her yew distaff and set out up to her shieling, to seek a kid from her flock which had gone astray. She returned at the midnight hour and, on passing the small graveyard above the pool at Baile na Cille, saw that all the graves within its walls were opened and the souls departed the while. She waited an hour and observed spirits returning, young and old, dark and fair, with each grave closing upon the returning spirit, clean as if it had never been opened. One grave, outside the burial walls, lacked a headstone. It remained open after all the others had closed. Margaret was curious: a grave outwith the graveyard wall signified disgrace, suicide or some unusual circumstance of death. Acting upon a strange compulsion, she threw her stout distaff across the grave so that it could not close, and waited. After some time a spirit returned, finely clothed and with its long fair hair shining and streaming in the moonlight. Margaret demanded of it why it returned so long after the others.

"My journey was lengthier than theirs," it replied, "for I had to go many leagues to the islands of Norway. I am the ghost of Princess Gradhag of Lochlin, drowned here on the sands of Uig Bay. Let me to my rest."

In that moment Margaret recalled the prophecy of the fetch from years before. She realised that this must be her chance to perform an act of courage that would hold a princess to ransom. As boldly as she could she spoke: "First you must give me a ransom of worth."

"I have no gold," cried the spirit, "let me to my rest."

"You keep the Stone – a blue Seeing Stone. I must have it from you."

"You are a woman of courage and welcome to the Stone, but I warn you, it was the cause of my death and of others of my line before me."

It was as if Margaret could neither hear nor heed this dreadful warning. She pressed the ghost of the Princess further, who told her how the Seeing Stone was to be found in the pool at Baile na Cille. When the instructions were complete, Margaret removed the yew distaff. The ghost stood before her, a gleaming spirit in the dark night, and spoke urgently: "Another strand joins now in the knot that is the Stone. Beware that you are not caught, as I was, in the coils of its twisting." With that the Princess of Lochlin sank into her grave, and Margaret watched the earth close over her like a dark wave.

At dawn Margaret ventured down to Baile na Cille, reaching the sands at ebb tide. She was drawn straight to the spot where the Stone lay. Lifting it from the pebbled pool floor she found that it fitted tantalisingly into the curve of her hand but, mindful of the warning from her fetch all those years ago, she did not raise it to her eye.

On the Nature of Second Sight

There is nowhere in the world where second sight is as strong in its manifestation as on the island of Lewis. There is some debate and conjecture among those who study these matters as to whether second sight is derived from a peculiarity of the island or of its people. The evidence is uncertain. In support of the contention that it is the place, not the people, it has been noted that when Lewismen with strong sight travel abroad, their capacities are much reduced.

∞

Duncan Smith of Tolsta was so afflicted with second sight that he was unable to keep his visions from intruding into every moment of his existence. He could not pass a stranger upon the road without seeing a dozen episodes yet to come in the stranger's life. Burdened by the intrusion of these visions he became mad and was taken to live under the care of his sister, who had married a man from Aberdeen. Once away from Lewis, Duncan's visions subsided and he was able to live a normal life. Some years later he came back to the island to settle affairs after his father's death and immediately his second sight returned and he was again incapacitated.

∞

Second sight is made the more powerful if its vision is seen whilst using a seeing stone. Some of the wisest authorities believe that seeing stones do not, of themselves, produce the vision. The vision lies within the seer and not within the stone. Others dispute this, arguing that the long, and sometimes malevolent, history of the great seeing stones must suggest that the stones themselves hold the power of foretelling. They strengthen this contention with examples of individual stones known to have transcended time and place as if driven by a malicious future purpose. Foremost among these stones with an independent power of prophecy is the Brahan Stone, also known as the Tostesson or Lochlin Stone.

∞

Although accomplished seers may summon second sight at will, for most who have it the ability to see lies outside their control. Most with the sight regard it as an affliction. Second sight is partly, but not entirely, passed down within a family by lineal descent. Often it may skip a generation, sometimes two. It is descended through the female line, accounting for the fewer numbers of men who possess it. When a man has the sight, however, it will be strong, a fact borne out by the experiences of many notable prophets including the Brahan Seer himself.

∞

Second sight is at its most strong, and its most reliable, when the same vision is seen by several people. There are well-attested cases of fishermen's wives who, each at the identical instant in their own homes, have seen a shipwreck. They have rushed distraught from their doors, to find themselves among others who had also seen the same fearful vision. Inevitably, and without fail, such shared visions of calamity have proved true and the husbands, sons and brothers of the unfortunate women have never returned from their fishing.

∞

Although the most frequent manifestation of second sight is in the form of a vision, both sounds and smells may equally appear as portents. The *taisk*, or cry of death, which is sometimes called a wraith, is heard as a chilling wail and is a certain warning of an imminent death nearby.

∞

The speed with which a vision of the future is fulfilled is said to depend on the time of day it appears to the seer. A morning vision will come to pass sooner than a vision later in the day. Night seeings are said to require the longest period for fulfillment, often months or even years. This is only true for involuntary visions that appear without warning to the unaccomplished seer.

∞

At the selfsame moment that Kenneth Odhar, the Brahan Seer, met his fate in a barrel of flaming tar at Chanonry Point, more than a hundred women of Lewis were said to be afflicted with visions of fire and darkness. That same day, fires smelled of charred flesh and the odour was so rank that people extinguished their hearths rather than *smor* them for the night.

∞

Horses and dogs can have second sight, but it has never been reliably observed in sheep. Some have suggested that goats have the sight because it has been repeatedly verified that when a person possessed by the sight looks intently towards an object or vision, the goats in the vicinity all turn their heads in that same direction.

∞

Lord Tarbat was scornful of superstition and dismissed all accounts of second sight. While on Her Majesty's business in Ross-shire, he was resting in an armchair within a house when a commotion outside disturbed his peace. He sent one of his retinue to enquire the cause of the disturbance and was informed that it was a seer with second sight who had foreseen that a great misfortune would occur that day to a man sitting in that very chair. The seer begged His Lordship to vacate the chair forthwith to forestall the catastrophe. Lord Tarbat dismissed him as a superstitious fool and left to continue on his journey.

Less than an hour later, a member of Tarbat's retinue fell from his horse and was gravely injured. He was taken back to the house and placed upon the same chair. The seer's prophecy was thus fulfilled, as Lord Tarbat himself testified to the chronicler Martin Martin.

∞

Second sight is beset with symbols, signs and portents. The meaning of many of these tokens is readily evident: a shroud foretells death as, similarly, does an empty chair. Other symbols are more obscure. A woman seen standing at a man's left hand will marry him within a year, but not if she stands on his right. In Lewis, second sight that includes a raven may be a portent of either good or ill. In Ireland the presence of a raven within a vision symbolises misfortune, whereas it is invariably a sign of good luck in the visions of the Norse people.

The Stone Stirs in Lochlin

MANY YEARS LATER in the island kingdom of Lochlin the Seeing Stone of Jarl Skule Tostesson, in some accounts, was once more safe in the possession of the ruling house. The Princess Gradhag, a descendent of that same royal line of Lochlin that bore the Princess Halldóra, took the Stone from its ancient yew box and dipped it in the pool where the high spring tide admitted wavelets to the entrance of Breakan's Cave. She rolled up a sleeve and reached down into the pool, carefully letting the Stone sink from her hand to rest among the pebbles strewn on the bottom. She sat back, keeping a watchful eye on the pool, as if she expected the Stone to escape. This was a ritual the Princess followed each spring tide, bringing the Stone to this pool so that the sea could renew its power. At the same time each month, cradling the yew box, she walked down to the sea from her father's hall past the rock called Halldóra's Leap. She did not know of the fateful things that had once come to pass here. In the years after those dire events, even the whisper of them was bad luck, so none spoke of what had transpired. Gradhag passed Breakan's Cave and Halldóra's Leap with no cognisance that these names stood as the final mute testament of a lovers' tragedy once wrought by her own Stone. In Lochlin, all memory of those sad occurrences had now been reduced to no more than place names. In Norway it was different, and on winter nights folk still told and retold the tale of the Evil Stone of Lochlin. Gradhag had not heard these tales and, were they to have reached her ears, she would not have recognised her Seeing Stone in them. For the Stone had brought her nothing but good. She was now in the seventh year of seeing with its aid.

Princess Gradhag was known throughout the island world as a seer of worth, and her advice was much sought. With the Stone's help she gave reliable counsel on where to find rich shoals of fish, or which crops would prosper. Tomorrow men from the Faroe Islands would arrive to consult her about favourable dates for the building of a monument. Her growing fame was pleasing to Gradhag, not from pride but because it gave her a worth of her own. It was a heaviness to be the daughter of a king. All would treat a princess with diffidence and respect, whether or not it was deserved, and from her earliest years she had been surrounded by the flattering tongues of those who wished to curry favour with her father. Now, as her foretelling skills and her artful use of the Stone became more widely known, Gradhag felt herself rising above the limitations of her royal life.

She continued to watch over the Stone as it soaked in the rock pool. The first blustery makings of a storm blew in from the sea and this caused her loose golden hair to stream and tug in the wind like delicate weed in the current. The pool's surface became an ocean of tiny waves and she could barely discern the outline of the Stone through the frenzy of ripplings. As she bent down, the better to see, Gradhag was startled that now, despite the increasing wind, the surface of the pool had become suddenly flat as glass. Her perfect reflection stared up at her with such clarity that, for a moment, it appeared to her that she was seeing herself in the pool, lying beneath the water, her pale face unmoving and her hair wafting and eddying like kelp to the waves. She reached down for the Stone and pulled it quickly from the pool, reassuring herself that the water's unnatural calm must have been created by the Stone that she might discover it more easily among the other rocks. Before replacing it in its box, the Princess brushed aside her streaming hair and held the Stone briefly to her eye. Through it she glimpsed the same glassy, drowned image of herself that she had just seen in the pool.

The following day Gradhag received the men of the Faroes and gave them auspicious advice. Her father the King was present, since the visitors were men of substance and their seeking of advice was a reflection of the esteem in which Lochlin was held, but he said nothing. The next day he summoned his daughter and she went to him, unsure why she had been called. He greeted her in a kindly manner and admitted that he had been observing her seeings now for some time. The King told her that, when it was known she had first discovered the Stone, he had been unsure whether to let her retain it for herself. He explained that he had thought for a moment it might be the lost Stone captured generations ago from Jørgen Oddmundsen, an enemy of Lochlin. Oddmundsen's family were great; their fortune came from sorcery and from using a seeing stone that had guided them well since the days of Jarl Skule Tostesson. But, he went on, he considered it unlikely that this could be the Stone and so he had let her use it for amusement. Now, however, he had begun to believe that this might indeed be the lost Stone. He had watched her power with it and had decided that the time had come to put the Stone to work for Lochlin. For a moment the Princess Gradhag pictured herself as her father's trusted adviser, using the Stone to steer him to great deeds and to build Lochlin above all rival kingdoms.

"Father, it has been my greatest hope that you would call upon me to use the Stone in the service of our country," she began. But her hopes were dashed as the King went on: "Because the Stone has proved its power, I have sent for a wise Seer from Björkö.

55

He is named 'Birka of the One Eye'. He will use the Stone under my direction to foresee favourable conquests."

Gradhag was crushed by her father's lack of faith in her. She knew her skills in foretelling to be reliable, and the Stone had become her constant companion and tool. She grieved to be parted from it.

"Father, have I not shown you my skill with the Stone, these several years?" Gradhag protested. "Have I not earned the right to be your adviser?"

"Skill you have shown," the King conceded, "in the matter of harvests, marriages and propitious foretellings. But matters of state are different. They are about war and great risk. They are men's work."

Gradhag knew that her father would brook no further argument. She was a dutiful daughter and when the one-eyed seer arrived in Lochlin, she handed over the Stone without protest. Birka of the One Eye had been forewarned that this could be the great Stone of Jarl Skule Tostesson and was cautious in his approach to it. He entreated the King to postpone its next use until the approach of winter, so that he could purge the Stone of any possible malice by immersing it alternately in fire and ice. But the King would have none of that, saying that his daughter had used it for seven years without harm, so there could be nothing to fear. One-eyed Birka did, however, take other precautions. He rubbed the Stone with a salve that dissolved evil; he placed a sprig of yew through its seeing hole and he cast runes to tell which hour of day would be propitious for a first seeing. Finally he could delay no longer. In the presence of the court, the Stone was brought forth in its battered yew box and the King asked a first question of the seer.

"It is my intent to raid the Orkneys. Can you see within the Stone a favourable outcome for this venture?"

One-eyed Birka, dressed in his necromancer's apparel, and

with amulets around his neck to protect him, slowly lifted the Stone to his blind eye. After a long silence, during which the whole court waited in great expectation, he took the Stone from his eye and said, "I see only a far-off pool where a peaty river frets at the edge of the sea."

The King urged him on. "A girl can coax more than you from this pebble," he growled, "I do not doubt that you can do better. Raise it once more."

Birka raised the Stone once more to his blind eye. "Again I see a pool at the edge of the sea," he said, "and, floating therein, something I cannot well discern save that it is golden and it wafts and weaves in the water."

The King grew impatient. "Hold the Stone to your good eye," he urged. Anxiously Birka protested, telling the King that a stone's vision had greater truth if seen through a blind eye because a blind eye had only foresight and could not be swayed by present sight. Now the King became angry. "My daughter has two good eyes and the Stone serves her well. Obey me and raise it to your good eye." The Seer turned pale but finally, at the King's insistence, put the Stone to his good eye. He was silent for a moment and the court again held its breath in anticipation. Then Birka of Björkö gave out a mighty cry and cast the Stone from him. Clutching his good eye, he fell to the floor. Courtiers rushed to him and saw immediately that the Stone had blinded him. His eye had become the colour of ewe's milk.

After some days, Birka of Björkö recovered sufficiently to return, blind, and full of deep resentment, to the island of Björkö, taking with him a new tale of the Evil Stone of Lochlin that for generations would be winter's talk around many fires. It was soon common knowledge throughout Björkö that the Stone of Tostesson had awakened, full of malevolence.

Gradhag and her father knew nothing of the reputation for malice that the Stone was gathering across the far Northern Sea.

The King, nevertheless, realised that the Stone was too powerful a force to be left in its battered old yew box and so he caused a stronger box to be built to contain it. The new box, also of yew wood, had a stout lock commissioned from the finest locksmith in Lochlin. Its key was fashioned with an intricate silver head in the form of a Celtic knot. The silversmith was from Tara and used only enchanted silver from the royal mine. He created the knot from silver strands that he first passed through the Stone's hole before melting them and, in doing this, he ensured that there would be an enduring bond between key and Stone.

In its new yew box, the Stone remained undisturbed, locked securely, waiting and waiting.

On the Nature of Celtic Knots

This is a knotted tale and it begins, twists and ends as knots do. Knots are of ancient and obscure origin. It is said that the gods gave them to mortals to lift them above other creatures, for only humans can tie even the simplest of them. There is a knot in the Staff of Mercury and the oldest of runes have knots of unknown meaning.

∞

Although they contain riddles and mysteries within them, Celtic knots are not to be solved. They are intricacies to be explored. They should be approached with a quiet mind.

∞

The devil has never yet learned how to put a knot in a thread for sewing and, in consequence of this, his stitching will always unravel from the cloth. He can never learn the tailor's trade. Celtic knots make him dizzy and will drive him off.

∞

A Celtic knot has no beginning and no end. It is contained within itself. The uncle of Skule Tostesson, the Great Jarl of Norway, was imprisoned for 40 years within a knot for stealing from the gods. He wandered the maze from which there is no escape until he became mad. The knot-maker breathes life into the knot and seals it there at the moment the two ends of its construction are finally joined. The life held safe within the knot will live forever, as there is no entrance through which death can claw. To cut a knot is to kill its life and ill-luck

will follow in proportion to the life that has been lost. The great knot of Cairness was powerful with life when it was slashed by Viking raiders. Their five fine ships were soon thereafter destroyed in a ferocious storm and all souls were lost, including the daughter of a king.

∞

A knot may safely be cut with a silver knife at the midnight of a new moon. Or, if it is woven, it may be unpicked thread by thread. The last thread must be parted by blowing upon it.

∞

There is life within knots plaited by the great masters, flowing like flaxen braids tugging in the current.

∞

Knots are patterns toying with the comfort of repetition; they weft and warp an appearance of regularity. This gives them an illusion of simplicity.

∞

Knots hold no answers, but the finest of them draw the eye into profound questions; they unsettle and they reassure. T'mira McBeg of Hadreg, whose mother was a selkie, wove knots of great subtlety. On nights when the moon was full she would walk along the shore and vanish from sight among the rocks. On the day following she would weave so surely and so fast that her hands were a blur. Envious rivals followed her one midsummer night, hoping to learn

her secret. Watching from the cliffs
above, they saw her swim naked in the
moonlight through a forest of kelp,
twisting like an eel and no strand touched
her even the once.

∞

It is said that pregnant women cannot
be delivered if a knot remains tied
in the birthing room; even the most
rudimentary apron knot must be untied.

∞

The Blue Men, who dwell beneath
the uneasy seas of the Minch, plait
giant knots from the sea itself. They
collect and fashion streams of green,
blue, white and grey waters. When the
Minch roils unexpectedly, even upon
the calmest of days, you know they are
at work. These knots cannot hold long
and their unravelling gives the Minch
its ever-changing hues. It is said that the
Blue Men use knots in the conjuring of
storms.

∞

A triple knot of long-stemmed thyme,
flax and rosemary prevents the spread
of plague.

∞

Knots are as legends. They repeat and
they change; they wander and return;
they tell and they are retold. This book
is itself such a telling and retelling.

Of Malice and Poison

THERE IS A DIFFERENT TELLING of the tale giving an alternative account of how the Stone came into the possession of the Seer of Brahan. It begins beneath the peat on the estate of the Earl of Seaforth, along the border between Lewis and Harris. Kenneth of Seaforth was a labourer there. Although he did not know of this, he was descended from Kenneth MacKenzie, Baron of Kintail, who once ruled all Lewis. The descent was the result of a liaison between the Baron and a girl from Rodel. This lineage was known to a few but not spoken of. It had, nevertheless, given rise to some small and discreet preferments for the family of Kenneth. The factor of the estate was Charlie Macaulay, a good man of a jovial nature, who lived with his young wife, Elizabeth, in a fine farm house overlooking the island of Shiphoirt which stands in the great sea loch. The business of the estate took Macaulay away to Stornoway for long periods. In his absence, Elizabeth oversaw day-to-day affairs and directed Kenneth and three other estate workers in the performance of their duties.

Kenneth was young, willing and had the strength of two oxen. Elizabeth liked him well and often brought food to him as he laboured on the different parts of the estate. They talked much, and as may readily happen with too much talking, they grew together more than they should. Once, on an evening when Charlie was away, Elizabeth feigned fear of being alone in the large house and called Kenneth from his small cottage to guard over her. In Lewis, as in all islands, no act goes unseen and wagging tongues soon reported to Charlie Macaulay that his wife and Kenneth might be fond. Charlie's good nature caused him to think little of this gossip; instead, he thanked Kenneth for the care he showed Elizabeth, adding that he was fortunate to have so trustworthy a young man on the estate. Kenneth was much affected by this declaration and vowed fervently to himself that henceforth he would allow nothing amiss in his meetings with Charlie's young wife.

Early in the summer, Charlie was summoned to meet the Earl in Inverness. Knowing that leaving the island would be a journey of many days, he enjoined Kenneth to take good care of his wife and he made preparation for a lengthy absence.

After her husband's departure, Elizabeth became ever more friendly toward Kenneth. One day she dispatched him to a distant part of the estate for peat cutting. He felt great relief within himself that he would be far from the grasping fingers of temptation and the gossiping tongues of the estate. It was a hot day and the work of cutting peat was hard, even to those who had the knack of it. He sweated and laboured and sweated more. Soon, this being a deserted part of the estate and with only his dog there to see him, he took off his clothes and cut all the cooler without them. Kenneth was so intently caught in the rhythm of his slicing that he failed to see Elizabeth until she was almost upon him. In shame and confusion he grabbed for his clothes but she laughed and said that she liked him the better without them. Indeed, she suggested, she would do the same, for the journey up to the peat bank to bring him food had made her hot. She began to disrobe but Kenneth averted his eyes, pulling on his clothes as he hopped away down the slope, until, red-faced and trembling he reached his cottage.

That evening she came to him at his cottage as if nothing of note had taken place up at the peats. Kenneth, who had been in a state of torment all that afternoon, could not bring himself to look her in the eye. She made a further declaration of a forward nature and Kenneth warned her that he believed it his avowed duty to resist her advances and, on her husband's return, to inform him of these unfortunate events. She was overcome with panic and, when her repeated entreaties failed to move him, she flew into a rage. Elizabeth cursed him soundly, saying she was determined that her husband would never be told of what had transpired.

Next day the young woman came once again bearing food to where Kenneth was digging the peats. Her demeanour was now more modest and, with a downcast look, she begged him to forget all the foolishness that had gone between them and to say nothing to her trusting husband Charlie. But Kenneth was stubborn in his virtue and, believing that a sin once committed cannot be so readily withdrawn, declared that he was compelled to reveal the wrong to Charlie Macaulay. Now Elizabeth became enraged beyond imagining and vowed the death or ruin of young Kenneth.

Next day, troubled and anxious, he once more shouldered his spade and trudged with his dog to the peat beds. Through the hot day he worked undisturbed, for Elizabeth did not appear with food. He was much relieved by her absence and counted his hunger a small price to pay. On the following day, after a troubled night, he again returned to the peat bed resolving to dig deep and dig well. He set to the spade with a will and made good progress. After several hours, however, Kenneth became tired. He sat down against the wall of peat to take a rest and, in consequence of several anxious and sleepless nights, he allowed himself to stretch out on the ground and fell into a fitful slumber. Soon he was awakened by some hard object that pressed against his ribs. He looked down and found that it was a stone, pale and rounded, with a perfect hole in it. Picking it up the young man marvelled at the smoothness of it and how well it fitted into his hand with an exactness that a clockmaker would envy. Kenneth examined the perfect regularity of the hole and, in doing so, held it to his eye. He was aghast to perceive Elizabeth within the circle of its seeing. It was several minutes before he trusted himself well enough to look again. This time he saw her in the barn reaching for the jar of arsenic that her husband used in the making of summer sheep dip. There she was, sprinkling the poison liberally into a bowl of stew. Kenneth watched her covering the bowl and calling for Rory, a shepherd on the estate, telling him he must hasten to take the bowl to the peat beds. Kenneth could not credit what he had seen and stayed in a stupor of disbelief, the Stone still cradled in his hand. In time Rory appeared from below, bearing a covered bowl. Kenneth was still unable to imagine the malice that the Stone had revealed to him. A part of him wished to believe that he was mistaken and that, should he dare to eat the stew, all would be well. But a quiet voice within him counselled caution and he permitted his dog to feed from the bowl instead. Within minutes the poor creature died, in an agony of writhing.

Kenneth seized the Stone and, his heart beating almost to bursting, ran back to his cottage and gathered together his meagre effects, tying them in a bundle. With a new-found purpose he marched past Elizabeth, who stood there, white-faced and frightened at what she had done. As he reached her he said, "When Charlie Macaulay returns it would be better that you were lying in the peat bed with my dog, than have to face the disgrace which is coming to you." And with that, young Kenneth of Seaforth, later to be known to all as the Brahan Seer, made his first foretelling and strode out into the world.

On the Nature of Twists in the Knot of Time

Time is like a Celtic knot. It is without beginning or end and has much intricate twisting along its path.

∞

Time may turn back upon itself and, in so doing, will cross its own tracks. At the point of this crossing strange places will seem familiar and conversations appear to have taken place once already. The past and the future may come together for a moment. It has befallen many – setting out on a journey – to see, on the outward path, a figure coming towards them. When the apparition nears they see it is themselves upon the return and, at that moment of recognition, the figure vanishes.

∞

Stone circles were built in the olden times to mark the spots where time twists or loops upon itself. Such places have magic and power. There are also areas, though they are said to be very few in number, where the thread of time makes many crossings of itself, becoming a knot within a knot. Strange events will happen here. Such a place is the pool at Baile na Cille on the sands of Uig.

∞

The circle of time may wait many years to loop back upon itself. The seer Kenneth Odhar is reliably said to have made predictions during a lifetime that, from the best historical accounts, must have exceeded three centuries. Some explain this in the following manner: Kenneth was able to live the span of several lifetimes by returning in old age to Baile na Cille. There, by standing at an exact spot revealed to him by the Stone, he would step across between the strands of time and once again become the young Kenneth and in this manner his life would be renewed. In regaining his youth, he was able to bring with him a prior lifetime's wisdom. Each renewal made him ever wiser, accounting in part for his extraordinary capabilities.

∞

The threads of time have no beginning and no end, but fearsome storms or wizardry may fray a strand and it may part. Any mortal venturing along a parted strand of time will disappear or die.

∞

When two strands of time run alongside one another, they will tell differing accounts of the same tale of life. Should they come close, by inadvertence or by art, it is possible to step from one to the other. A girl from Eadar dha Fhadhail, being 'the place between two waters', now known as Ardroil, was seen crossing the sands at Uig, weeping for the loss of her sweetheart who had been drowned that very day. She vanished from the sands and it was believed that, careless with grief, she had wandered into the sea and been swept away. But she appeared to her sister in a dream and told her she had stepped into another strand of time where her sweetheart was safe and that she had resolved to stay there forever.

∞

Time does not move solely to the tick of a clock. It travels more slowly on winter nights and makes them longer.

∞

Unique among all places in the world is the forbidden island of Svar, fifty leagues to the west of Lochlin. This island, being located at an inflection in the knot of time, has nights – in winter and in summer – that each last for a year. In consequence of this, a party of fishermen wrecked there for thirty days and nights had aged by thirty years when they were rescued by another boat. When they returned home, people marvelled at the change in them and Hadric, King of Lochlin, forbade any to venture again to the island of Svar.

∞

It is told that young Finlay MacRitchie disappeared from Breanish for seven years, his family thinking him drowned the while. One day he returned and, to the joy of his family and to the amazement of all, was in robust health and not one day older than the day he vanished. He related that, by an unfortunate happenstance, he had wandered into a looping of time that had made itself into a circle.

Each day repeated the day before. Each morning he would catch the same fish with a damaged fin; the rain would come at the exact same moment each day. In the afternoon, as he wandered below the cliffs seeking an escape, the same sheep would slip on the rocks and fall at his feet. Every day a raven would come seeking food and would accept three morsels from his hand. Out at sea he could make out a boat far off that never

responded to his daily waving and cries. Each night he slept fitfully, making plans but, upon the next day, was compelled to relive what had gone before.

After seven years, when he had despaired of any escape, the raven spoke to him saying, "You have fed me every day for seven years and, in reward, I will lead you from this circle back to your destined thread of time." Following the raven Finlay found himself on the road at Mealista, scarcely a mile from his home in Breanish.

Prelude to a Raid

S CHOLARS OF CONSIDERABLE NOTE have engaged in lively debate on the matter of the Stone's malevolence. Some contend, and with good reason, that it foretells evenhandedly. In support of this contention, they will show that the Stone, in most tellings of the tale, gives Princess Gradhag fair warning of her own drowning. Others will counter that darker versions of the tale contain irrefutable evidence of ill will. They argue that the Brahan Seer himself must have known of the Stone's malevolence, otherwise why would he, in so many of the tellings, make his final act the casting of the Stone into Loch Ussie, intending to be rid of it?

Some Norse folklorists divide the threads of the tale which weave through Lochlin into summer and winter versions; in the former the Stone is the more benign. In the darkest of the winter tellings there is no princess and the Stone holds in thrall successive generations of the ruling house of Lochlin, all of whom are either driven mad by it or meet terrible and violent deaths.[5] The story which now follows is from a summer version, although its end is characteristically tragic, and it is still told across the world wherever the old tongues are spoken. It incorporates many elements of other versions, yet is imbued with unique elements that make it crucial for any who wish to understand the Stone and its heritage.

It was the sixth year of the reign of King Hadric, a time of peace. Yet Hadric's heart was not at ease. Although he styled himself 'King of Lochlin', he knew that some mocked him. None openly denied his right to rule Lochlin; that right had been firmly established by lineage and by treaty. But to style himself 'King' was whispered by some to demean the other royal houses of the north, for Lochlin had fallen upon hard times and the country was poor. It had come to Hadric's ear that he was called 'the Beggar King' at the wedding of the Prince of Hedemark, amid much ribaldry, and this was a great affront to him. His dearest wish was to restore the fortunes of his line. He dreamed that history might style him 'Hadric the Great' and consider his reign the opening of a new and prosperous age. He could not know that in times to come he would be known as 'Hadric the Hesitant'.

Hadric was indeed a cautious man although, in his circumstances, caution and wisdom went hand in hand. The greatest enrichment came from conquest, yet his power was too slender and his coffers too slight to support a war. Raiding was another possible course he mulled over. Nearby opportunities were few and the easy pickings long gone. Any raid must be far afield and that required stout ships. In times past, Lochlin had been famed throughout the north for its master shipwrights and, while the skill of shipcraft remained, of late there had been little employment in the shipyards. On the night of the spring solstice, Hadric had a dream. In his dream he saw a fleet of fine ships being built in Lochlin. These ships were of an exact and detailed design and every constituent element of their construction was etched vividly into his mind. In his dream, the ships ploughed far and fast, returning from unknown lands laden with treasures. He basked in the awe of rival kingdoms. He became rich beyond any of his neighbours; his daughter Gradhag was betrothed to the Prince Eirik of Uppsala, whose wealth and power was legendary.

When he woke from this dream, Hadric was filled with unaccustomed purpose. He summoned the master shipwrights of Lochlin to meet him. They worked together to fashion a new ship with a deep keel and sails of an intricate and hitherto unknown design. Great was the excitement raised by Hadric's vision and word soon spread to neighbouring kingdoms that something momentous was afoot in Lochlin. These tales reached the island of Björkö where a seer dwelt named 'Birka of the One Eye'.[6] Birka had never journeyed to Lochlin, neither had he met King Hadric. But he was struck by a great compulsion to go forthwith to seek audience with the King and to offer himself to Hadric as his seer. He had strong second sight, although he did not *see* that he would himself soon be caught in a looping of the tale that would lead him to ill-fortune.

Arriving in Lochlin, Birka was well received by the King. The seer did not know it, but Hadric's old caution was now returning to him. His nights had become sleepless again and disturbed by fearful thoughts. What if he built the fine ships but they discovered no treasure? What if other kingdoms attacked him and took his vessels? What of shipwrecks? He had decided, that very morning, to find a seer who could foretell a secure course and guide him to safety in the ventures ahead. He had been considering employing for this purpose his own daughter, the Princess Gradhag, who had acquired a substantial reputation for her abilities to see with an ancient and powerful stone. Such thoughts were stilled by the arrival of the one-eyed seer from Björkö. Hadric declared to Birka his surprise and pleasure that, on the very day he found himself wishing for a seer, one should land upon his shores. Both men believed they were favoured by good fortune as a result. Hadric was a king famed for caution and Birka a seer gifted with second sight but, naturally, neither yet suspected malice in the force that had caused their meeting.

72

Hadric brought forth the yew box and from it lifted the Stone. The King handed it to Birka, and told the seer that it was believed to be the famed Stone of Jarl Skule Tostesson. The seer had heard many accounts of this Stone and, because several of the tales ascribed it with evil intent, he became wary. The Stone tempted him because, if it were indeed Tostesson's Stone, then it could bring him great power. But still Birka hesitated. He stood still, gazing at the pale stone in his hand, longing to lift it to his eye and yet fearful. The King saw his uncertainty. "It is meant to be," he reassured the seer, "for why else would you have been summoned here?"

Birka slowly raised the Stone to his blind eye. After a long silence, during which the King waited expectantly, he took the Stone from his eye and said, "I see only a pool where a peaty river frets at the edge of the sea."

The King urged him on. "My daughter can coax more than you from this Stone," he whispered, "I do not doubt that you can do better. Raise it once more."

Birka raised the Stone again to his blind eye and this time saw the same pool with something in it that had the appearance of locks of fair hair, or golden kelp, wafting in the current.

"Hold the Stone to your good eye," the King commanded.

Birka of Björkö hesitated for a long moment, as if in a trance. He turned milky pale and, reaching for the yew box, replaced the Stone very deliberately once more in its cradle. "I felt the knot of time turn on this moment," he said. "There is only bad fortune here for me and for Lochlin." And he refused to be drawn further.

King Hadric was enraged. The way forward, so nearly in his grasp, had been snatched from him by the superstitions of a seer. He ordered his guards to whip Birka soundly and banished him from Lochlin. When the seer, after many miseries, set foot once again on the island of Björkö, he was embittered by his harsh treatment and vowed revenge on Hadric. He cast runes and entered the seeing trance. In this state he saw five splendid ships being built in the shipyards of Lochlin. They were unguarded and, as he watched, Birka saw raiders from Orkadal coming to take them. When he returned from the trance he knew that the loss of these five ships would hurt the King who had become his enemy more sorely than any other misfortune.

Björkö was a trading place and ships from many lands sojourned there. One of them was a vessel from Orkadal, whose captain sought the seer to give a foresight of weather in the straits to the mainland. Sensing the propitiousness of the captain's visit, the seer revealed to the astonished man that he knew of five richly appointed ships in Lochlin – better than any yet made – which would be easy prey, being as yet unprotected. Further, he told him that he had foreseen men from Orkadal taking the ships and becoming rich from the seizure. The captain was a man of deeds and accustomed to grasping at opportunities. He urged Birka to return with him to Orkadal, to raise with him a raiding fleet to capture the Lochlin ships.

In Lochlin, King Hadric was cast into indecision and gloom after the seer's expulsion. He found he was afraid to go forward, fearing the ill-fortune that Birka of the One Eye had foreseen. Yet his ambition to restore his kingdom remained great. After some thought he decided to test his daughter and her Stone. He chose a simple question for her seeing. He asked when the ships would be launched, knowing from his shipwrights that this event was to be thirty days off. Princess Gradhag put the Stone to her eye and saw the launching a full two months hence. The King, believing her wrong, scorned her foretelling, saying it was too inexact for his purpose, as he knew full well that the launch was to be within the month. Gradhag coolly replied that it would indeed take two months because all work must cease while preparation was made to defeat the raiders who would come from Orkadal. Lowering the

Stone she turned her gaze upon the King: "Birka of the One Eye from Björkö is plotting, together with a fleet of Orkadal pirates, to seize your fine ships."

Hadric felt despair at this news. He had no army and few guards. The ships had become his dearest joy, the emblems of his hope for the kingdom, and their loss would crush the fortunes of Lochlin. But the Princess lifted the Stone once again and foresaw that the shipwrights would cover the ships with branches so that they could not be seen from the sea. Then, on the open sands, they would begin to construct five new ships of meagre quality. They would be working on these poor vessels when the raiders arrived.

Hardly daring to hope, King Hadric ordered the shipwrights to do as his daughter had instructed. Their swift ships, now nearing completion, were soon covered with hay, kelp and branches so artfully that only the most discerning eye could detect them. The builders then chose a promontory that would be seen by any approaching vessel and there they hastily began to cobble together five impoverished hulks, scarcely better than wrecks.

In due time the fleet from Orkadal arrived, as the Stone had foretold. The crews and Birka leapt ashore and surveyed the shipwrights' work. Never had they seen such poorly-built ships, with not the one worth taking. In a fury, the men from Orkadal dragged the one-eyed seer along the beach to Breakan's Cave, beneath the rock called Halldóra's Leap. There they punished his poor foresight by pouring tincture of hellebore into his remaining eye until it turned the colour of ewe's milk and he was blinded completely.

The raiders returned to Orkadal and work resumed in Lochlin on King Hadric's marvellous ships. They were completed within the two months that the Princess Gradhag had foreseen. In consequence of her predictions with the Seeing Stone, the Princess Gradhag was raised high in her father's esteem and thereafter sat with him as his constant adviser.

On the Nature of Stout Ships

A stout ship is alive as the sea. There is life in her timbers and in the joints of her timbers. Her keel and the sea are lovers in the storm and in the harbour's gentle aftermath. Her planking breathes with the slow swell of a calm ocean.

∞

A good ship knows her name before she is made. Her name rustles in the leaves of the oaks from which she is hewn. A woman with second sight may press her ear to the great oak that will become the ship's keel and listen for a name. If the hearing is easy, a fortunate name will come and the ship will have luck.

∞

A stout ship must be taut but not stiff. She should creak to the groaning oars. Her shipwright must be an upright man, for a proud man makes a proud ship. Each day he must visit the sea and dip his adze into the waters three times. First, for the sea and the gods of the sea; second, for the spirits of sailors departed; third for the work of the carpenters.

When a carpenter toils, his bearing should be as the ship he is building. He, too, must be taut but not stiff. His sinews and joints must be as the sea and as the ship, swelling and straining in the heavy work, yet gliding gently in the finishing. The shipwrights of Lochlin make the finest ships, but even the stoutest of these cannot best a storm that has been woven by the Blue Men of the Minch.

∞

A stout ship is ever watchful, as women are watchful. She hears the squall before it comes. She tightens to the rising wind. When the gale keens through her rigging she sings back. When the evil spirits of the sea hear the song of a stout ship they cannot rise. Only the Blue Men of the Minch can challenge her.

∞

When a stout ship lies at anchor she is like a child asleep, gentle in her slumber. The sailors ashore in the tavern sing in her praise.

∞

A good ship is lively in her response. Sailors know a good ship for she moves with them like a partner. She senses the pitch of each wave. Her tiller strains against the steersman's arm like a horse eager to gallop.

∞

When the eldest son of Jarl Skule Tostesson came of age his father summoned him to speak together of kingship and affairs of war. "What is the most important thing a king must have?" his father enquired, testing the young man. The prince's reply was "stout ships", which pleased his father well.

∞

The treacherous Minch is best crossed by stout *longfhada*, longships, sometimes named lymphads, but the seamen of The Lews ply much of their commerce with

smaller craft called birlinns or, in the old
tongue, *byroingr*. Men of the mainland
lack the skills to safely sail birlinns.

Richard of Poolewe claimed himself to
be the best sailor on the entire west
coast of Scotland. He had seen birlinns
from Lewis safely cross the Minch into
Oban and Mallaig, even in the stormiest
winters, and reckoned he could well
match the seamanship of the Lewis
sailors.

With two companions, he thieved
a birlinn moored in the harbour of
Mallaig and they set sail for Lewis full
of jovial confidence. Scarcely had they
rounded the Point of Sleat, being the
southernmost part of Skye, when the
craft was tossed by squalls and began to
roll. Some leagues before reaching the
domain of the Blue Men of the Minch,
they decided to turn back. But the craft
yawed and pitched beyond control and
they all drowned. So it is well said that it
takes a Lewsman to sail a birlinn as if it
were a stout ship.

The Stone at Loch Ussie

MOST TELLINGS OF HOW THE STONE came into the hands of Kenneth Odhar, the Brahan Seer, cite the pool at Baile na Cille as marking the spot of its discovery. For these tales there is good provenance to show how the Stone reached the pool from Lochlin, bringing to the accounts a satisfying strand of continuity. In a number of other tellings, however, along a different thread of time, the Stone came into the possession of the Seer from a peat bed that lay a half hour's walk above Baile na Cille. But what brought the Stone to lie in this peat bed? There is an obscurity lurking here with few accounts proposed in explanation. One rendition of the tale that provides a possible path sets forth a turning in time that fetches the Stone from Loch Ussie. In this account, the Seer – many years hence – will cast his Stone into the loch at the moment of his arrest and betrayal by the Earl of Seaforth's lady. In so doing, time will reverse itself and an event in the future will become the direct cause of a happening in the past. For this reason some scholars regard the account as lacking credence. It is well to remember that there are many credible instances which show that the knot of time does turn upon itself at Baile na Cille and some believe that it turns there twice. So a telling cannot lightly be dismissed on the grounds that its end precedes its beginning.

One twist of this disputed tale began on the banks of Loch Ussie, on the Brahan estate near Strathpeffer in Ross-shire, where MacIver of Kintail had caught a great fish. MacIver was full of delight with his catch and shouted gleefully to his two companions. He was a large, clumsy man with a greatly enlarged right thumb, which usually made him an awkward fisherman. On account of his deformity his friends called him 'Two-Thumbs' and gently mocked his lack of dexterity.[7] So, for MacIver, there was an added satisfaction in reeling in such a large and unusual catch.

In shape, the fish was like a pike, but there was something unfamiliar about its form. MacIver and two of his companions surveyed it and speculated that none like it had been caught there before. For a moment they were unsure whether to eat it or take it to show their friends. They hesitated, but soon hesitation gave way to hunger and they sliced the fish open, intending to divide its flesh between them. In the stomach of the fish they found a pale stone, through the which ran a perfect hole. MacIver held this stone to the light and on its surface saw there were markings like old runes. None of the three could interpret runes, so the marks were no more to them than a moment's curiosity. MacIver, however, decided to save the stone and put it in his creel to show it to Alasdair MacKenzie, who was cousin to Lord Seaforth's factor and a man of wisdom and learning. MacIver hoped that MacKenzie would determine if the markings were a writing that could be deciphered.

That evening MacIver returned to his cottage with his portion of the fish and ate well. It was a long summer's evening and, after his meal, he sat in his doorway and took the stone from his creel. He idly observed the hole through it and brought it to his eye but saw nothing remarkable through it. That night he went to his bed, leaving the stone upon his table. He dreamt that he sat outside his cottage and held the stone to his eye. Through it, he perceived a raven flying towards his chimney. When he removed the stone, the raven turned into a magpie and flew away. In his dream he raised the stone again and once more saw the raven flying at him. Yet again he lowered the stone and the raven was transformed into a magpie and fled. MacIver did this a third time and, in his dream, the magpie began to call out warning words as it flew away. He tried to hear the bird's message but was suddenly awakened from his sleep by a crash. MacIver lit a candle and saw that the stone, though it had been placed in the centre of the table, had fallen inexplicably to the floor.

The next day MacIver once again held the stone in his hand for a long time but did not bring it to his eye, being uneasy about what his dream might portend. That night he could not sleep because the hand with which he had held the stone was gripped by pain and numbness. He rose and went to sit at his table where, in the long half-light of a summer dawn, he gazed at the strange stone. For a moment he dozed and was shocked awake by it crashing to the floor for a second time.

The third night MacIver placed the stone on the floor beneath the table, fearing that should he allow it to fall for a third time, it could be an ill omen. He retired to bed, hoping for sound sleep. Instead he found himself in the throes of a grim nightmare, in which he saw a wild-faced man casting the stone into Loch Ussie and loudly cursing the Seaforth line. The man was dragged away and was himself flung into a barrel of boiling pitch, terrible to see, where he writhed and died in the most fearful agonies. MacIver started awake in a sweat, deciding upon the instant to take the stone to the wise Alasdair MacKenzie and to seek his advice, for he was now fearful of impending ill-fortune. Bending beneath his table to retrieve the stone from the floor whence it had been left, he could not find it. He stood in puzzlement and then saw it, resting in the middle of the table. Because he had not touched the stone, he knew on the instant that its rising from the floor must be of a supernatural cause. In great agitation the anxious man gathered it up and took it to the house of Alasdair MacKenzie, waking him from sleep.

MacKenzie listened carefully to the story and looked closely at the stone. He took a reading glass from his cupboard and, for a long time, peered through it at the markings on the stone's surface. He started to speak but thought better of it and lapsed into deep thought. Finally he said, "I cannot make out the markings. If they be runes then they are ancient beyond my ken. I suspicion they may be knotted runes, so-called less for their shape than for the convolutions of the old tongue they represent. But other elements in your tale are omens and I like them not. First there is the raven. If a raven flies around a chimney it is a sure portent of death within the house. You came near death each time you held this pebble to your eye but, by lowering it, you narrowly escaped. In support of this contention, the magpie is a cheating bird and its appearance signifies that you have cheated death itself. The pain in your hand was because you were not meant to hold the pebble and I believe this to be true, because this is a seeing stone of undisputed influence and meant for the hand and eye of another. That the stone has supernatural power is beyond dispute, as its ability to move between table and floor must confirm. It was anxious to be elsewhere and you hinder its intent at your peril. Were it not for your third dream, I would advise you to toss it far into the loch from whence it came." He stopped and put his hand out to detain his frightened guest, who was already moving toward the door. "But it is my advice that you should *not* perform such an act, because your dream shows death to be the reward for him that throws it back. My counsel to you is to place this strange stone upon a black rock and there cover it well with yew branches. Leave it thereafter to its own fate, for it is my belief that the sooner you are rid of it the less you will become entangled in the misfortunes it may carry."

Alasdair MacKenzie was a wise man and his words, spoken so gravely, reassured MacIver that the proposed course of action would end the matter without harm. The young man did as MacKenzie instructed and no evil befell him thereafter. Being youthful and not given to great curiosity, he soon forgot the whole affair. He never knew that by the cast of his hook he had fulfilled a prophecy yet to be made and that, through him, time had turned back upon itself. Alasdair MacKenzie's mind, being of a reflective nature, often pondered in later years upon the meaning of that early morning, when a young man had pounded upon his door, white with fear and clutching a pale stone. He sensed that the seeing stone, whose strange markings he examined that day, had some great importance, but he could never reason what its meaning might be. Years from these strange events his life came to a peaceful close at his daughter's house in Strathpeffer, with him never knowing that the Brahan Seer was soon to cast the Stone into Loch Ussie, prophecying that it would be found in the belly of a fish and would pass into the hands of one whose power of foretelling would be equal to his own.

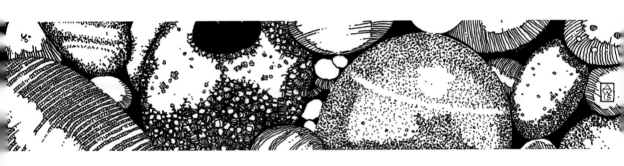

On the Nature of Ravens

In ancient times, ravens were divided into two clans, the larger clan being the black ravens, who fell afoul of the three giants of Lochlin. The giants put a curse upon them, in consequence of some supposed effrontery or theft. Black ravens were ever minded to steal the treasures of others and some have supposed that their offence was the theft of a seeing stone of great worth. The fortunes of the black ravens declined thereafter, the clan being unable to shake the curse.

The black ravens sank to scavenging, begging and thievery. They picked the flesh of warriors slain on the battlefield and, in all respects, were soon no better than common crows. The curse that had been put upon them had such power and endurance that there was scarcely an occasion that a black raven should cross the path of men but that ill luck would surely result. In this way ravens earned the repute of bringers of ill.

∞

The smaller clan, the grey ravens, was smiled upon by fortune. It is told that they were descended from the two ravens, Huginn and Muninn, who sat upon the shoulders of Odin and were his favoured spies. In return for their services, Odin gave the ravens fortune and second sight. Wherever a grey raven alighted, good luck would follow. But the promiscuous habits of the black ravens led to a mixing of the clans and in the present age it is oftentimes hard to determine whether a raven brings fortune or grief. This mixing has caused much debate among scholars as to the benevolence or the malevolence of ravens. Nonetheless, men who work the land tip their hats to all ravens so that they might not offend them.

∞

Among the Western Isles it is said that an infant will die if a raven's egg is stolen. When Donald MacKenzie came to Lewis from Kintail he scoffed at the superstition of a backward people and took ravens' eggs for his breakfast. He had three sons and each wasted and perished before completing his first year of life.

∞

Should a raven's egg be taken from the nest in order to procure some result, an instance being the removal of an egg to compel a raven to seek a seeing stone, the stolen egg must be boiled and replaced within the hour or ill-fortune will ensue.

∞

If the croak of a raven is heard during the preparation for a hunt this signifies that good fortune will accompany the hunting. The exception to this rule is during the hunting of seals. As an outcome of deliberations at the ravens' parliament, an agreement was reached with the seals that the birds would not be complicit in the provision for hunters of any fortunate omens concerning seals.

∞

Although it is nigh impossible to tell a grey raven from a black raven by sight, it is well attested that a grey raven has a span of life that greatly exceeds the life of his black cousin. If a bird is of direct grey raven descent, it will live for a hundred years and its memory is sharp and long.

∞

Calum MacKay was returning to Cirivig from Harris over the mountains. A fog descended around him and soon he was lost. He sat on a stone to wait for the fog to lift. A raven came and addressed him, saying, "Young Calum, you must continue your journey as this fog will endure for many days. I shall guide you in remembrance of your great-grandfather, Angus Mor, who once did me a kindness."

The raven showed him the path and Calum returned safely to Cirivig, whereas otherwise he would surely have languished in dire straits. Angus Mor, as his gravestone in the burial ground at Baile na Teampail testifies, had breathed his last a full eighty years before, so it can be surmised from this account that the bird had the pure grey raven bloodline.

∞

Ravens are efficacious in the telling of weather. If a raven turns into the wind and preens itself then it will rain. If a raven flies towards the sun this presages hot weather.

∞

King Cnut had a banner made from white silk that could foretell victory or defeat in battle. Although the banner had no device or picture upon it, when battle neared, the figure of a raven appeared as if interwoven within the cloth. If fortune intended to grant Cnut victory, the raven appeared with its beak wide and flapping its wings in triumph. If fate ordained defeat the raven drooped listlessly. In this way the King knew well when to engage the enemy and when to slip away unseen to avoid the engagement.

∞

It is a pretty custom of modern times to release two doves at a wedding. It is believed that if both fly off together, the marriage will be joyful; if they fly apart there will be strife. This is a worthless custom as doves are ever wont to fly as one and so the releasing gives a pleasing spectacle but is no true test. In former times, two ravens were released and the manner of their flying was an infallible prognosis of the happiness of the marriage.

The Two Pedlars

I T WAS MAY AND THE SUMMER WALKERS were setting forth from Inverness and Dundee, traversing the length of the Highlands and Islands to ply their wares. They were tinkers and tinsmiths, hawkers and horse-dealers, gypsies and pedlars. All summer long they would scour the countryside for trade, bringing with them stories and gossip aplenty. These walking folk were tellers of ancient tales, itinerant songsters and bards. They were also often rogues, scroungers and thieves but, because they were the very personification of summer, they were more welcome than not in the crofts.

Among their number was Glen Birrell, a pedlar from the Black Isle. He walked through the spring afternoon along the shores of Loch Ussie carrying his wares. He had a cargo of bright cotton cloth and high hopes that his goods would sell well in the west. His pack was heavy and he was tired. As was the way with pedlars, Glen's load was balanced by means of a band that ran around his forehead and, after many miles, he longed to loosen the straps and take respite. He saw a black rock on the shore that allowed him to rest the pack without bending and so he stopped and unbuckled his burden. The pedlar drank from the loch and stretched himself out on a patch of soft sand. Soon he fell into a weary sleep. As he awoke the first thing he saw was a small pile of dead yew branches on the rock, which he had not noticed when he first rested his pack there. The branches were loosely woven together, as if to conceal something. Moving them aside, Glen found a queer stone. It did not appear to him to be a thing of particular worth and he was inquisitive as to why anyone should think it of sufficient value to merit concealment. He saw that it had strange markings and, out of curiosity and compulsion, he placed it in the top of his pack together with the smaller wares as he prepared to trudge on.

Before long Glen fell in with Rab Robertson, another pedlar hailing from Inverness, who was bound for the island of Lewis with a pack of pegs, fishhooks and trinkets. This fellow was adept at stories and pedlar chatter, causing the miles to pass easily in his company. He was a teller of fantastic tales and he would narrate each one with such sober seriousness that it was hard to doubt the truth of what he said. Rab insisted that they should start early each day, which led to disputes between the two men, as his new companion was by preference a late riser. When Glen Birrell argued that there was no good reason to set out at dawn, Rab Robertson asked:

"If I could show you good reason, would you cease this constant carping?"

"Indeed," replied Glen, "but it seems unlikely that there could be any reason beyond your own preferences."

"Then I shall offer you proof absolute, showing that it is beneficial for you to start early in the day. Have you heard of Robert Addison, the great surveyor from your own home town of Inverness?"

Glen confessed that he was not familiar with the name.

"No matter," replied Robertson and, affecting a look of profound sincerity, launched into a tale. To add to the gravity of his words, he spoke them in a most serious manner.

"Robert Addison," he began, "was the best surveyor in all the

Highlands and, when he designated the true boundary between farms, only the most contentious neighbour would dare dispute it. He was possessed of an exact sense of distance, even without his measuring chain. One evening, returning from visiting a large farm that was to be split equally between four quarrelsome heirs, he sensed that the walking home, a distance of some seven miles, was longer than the walking there. Knowing this to be impossible, yet sensing it to be the truth, Addison determined to put his judgment to the test during each of the days that would be required to undertake the farm survey. Next morning, setting out early towards the farm, he drove a yew peg into the earth and, using his surveyor's chain, he and his apprentice measured out one exact mile of the seven-mile journey, driving in an iron stake to mark the precise spot where the mile ended. That evening, on their return journey, they found the iron stake and measured backwards from it to the yew peg. Their chain revealed that the return journey was longer by 77 feet. Addison repeated this procedure for seven days, each time finding that the returning distance was the greater by 77 feet, not an inch more, nor an inch less."

Sensing that he had intrigued his companion with this improbable tale, Rab Robertson continued to unfold his story in a serious and sincere tone:

"This discovery was greeted with scorn by younger surveyors, who strove to topple Robert Addison from the pedestal of high regard in which he was held. So they repeated his test for themselves and were astonished to find the same result. Moreover, they discovered that it was not only the return journey that was longer. Any mile, measured early in the morning, was shorter than that same mile measured late in the day. And it is for that reason we should start early, for we shall save ourselves distance and weariness."

"If this be true," protested Birrell, "then I should surely have heard of it!"

"Not so. The surveyors were dismayed by these findings, for

if any mile could be inexact by 77 feet, depending on the time of day, then the surveying profession would be in disarray and disrepute. And, for that reason, they each swore a solemn oath not to make the fact known, for the protection of their livelihoods."

Thereafter, the two pedlars agreed to start out each day at dawn.

Rab Robertson had many such stories, and he was a great dreamer. He had the intention, he explained, to become wealthy beyond imagination from his journey. He averred that no less an authority than the Brahan Seer had made a prophecy guaranteeing his fortune. He had committed the words of the prophecy to memory and recited them in a bold voice that would be the envy of many a bard: *When a key shall lie with a ring and a strange fish give forth a stone, then shall a pedlar on the Long Island gain such riches as shall fill a great ship.* Rab asserted, with cheerful confidence, that his mother, who was possessed of the second sight, had seen him as the pedlar in question and there could not be the slightest doubt that he was to be the beneficiary of the wealth that had been foretold. The Long Island, he explained, was Lewis in the northern part and Harris in the south, but his mother was confident that the fulfillment of the Seer's words would be found in Lewis and that the mentions in the prophecy of key, ring and fish were mere details to be disregarded. The unsuspecting Rab had no inkling that he was about to be caught in a loop of the knot of time when he would become the instrument destined to alter a dead man's childhood. Little did he know, as he declaimed the Brahan Seer's words to Glen Birrell, that, through a capricious reversal of time, he would soon be carrying a stone from the belly of a fish, or that a new-born boy lay awaiting his arrival on Lewis who would grow to be the Brahan Seer himself.

After some congenial days, the weather being fair, the two travellers reached Loch Garve, just before the village of Garve, where they rested at a pedlar's stone by the side of the water. Such flat rocks were commonly placed by pedlars as resting places to allow them to unburden themselves of the weight of their packs. Letting his talkative companion continue into Garve in hope of commerce, Glen Birrell rested his pack upon the rock to adjust his head strap. Weariness had made him careless. Without warning the heavy pack slipped, Glen's headband caught around his throat and when Rab returned an hour later, it was to find him dead, strangled by the weight of his own pack.[8] Rab Robertson was much affected by his unhappy discovery and by the loss of his new companion. He felt obliged to oversee the interment of his fellow traveller, even though it would entail a postponement in his own plans for enrichment. He sold the contents of Birrell's pack in Garve to defray the costs of a decent burial, which he organised in a sober and creditable way, eliciting favourable comment from those in the village whose opinions of pedlars had hitherto been low. It was while sorting the articles within the dead man's pack that Rab discovered the stone. He decided the trinket was of little value here but, because it might arouse some small interest on Lewis, he placed it within a bag of pegs in his own pack, hoping for some future opportunity to sell it on the island. Rab had heard that the people of Lewis were superstitious and put great store in the efficacy of seeing stones. For this reason he happily anticipated a profit, the more if he could romance some tale that this stone held special powers of divination.

When all rites for the unfortunate Birrell were decently completed and being careful not to display an unseemly haste to leave, Rab continued on his way westward until he reached the harbour at Mallaig. There he found a wretched and ill-founded vessel preparing to leave for the port of Stornoway. Rab Robertson was used to deprivation and indifferent to small discomforts, so he willingly shipped aboard, despite warnings called out by captains of rival vessels that the boat would assuredly go down in the stormy waters of the Minch.

Contrary to these dire predictions, when the vessel reached the sea, the waters of the Minch were unnaturally serene. The younger sailors joked that the Blue Men must be sleeping but an old hand on board warned otherwise. "The Blue Men never sleep," said he. "This calm is not natural. They let us pass for some terrible purpose we cannot guess." Rab Robertson said nothing but his heart was glad. He believed the smoothness of the waters showed that any ill omen he may have been carrying from the unhappy circumstances of Birrell's death would not stand in his way. He perceived the placid sea as confirmation of the Brahan Seer's prophecy and a sign that his path to wealth would now be smooth. In the port of Stornoway he stepped lightly ashore, shouldered his pack and started to walk towards the west. He had chosen fishhooks and clothes-pegs to carry, knowing that these items were always in high demand among the crofters. Though his pack weighed heavily upon his shoulders, he whistled cheerfully. He was unsure as to how he should become so mightily enriched but his confidence was unrestrained.

As Rab Robertson first set foot on the Isle of Lewis, a young mother was at work in a shieling in the hills above Baile na Cille preparing the first meal for her newly weaned son. She was a striking woman of dark complexion, with long red hair that had given rise to the name *Peigi Ruadh*, Red Peggy, by which she was known by all.[9] She was said to have selkie blood in her and some whispered that in a certain light her skin took on the sheen of a seal. She created an unease among the people of Uig. Peggy had the second sight and it was strong in her. She also had a babe whose father was unknown. Because this was an age before the new church would make such happenings shameful, the baby was more a matter of curiosity than of disgrace. But the boy added to Peggy's mystery and provided fuel to set idle tongues wagging. In her shieling she readied her child's meal, giving him ewe's milk from a raven's skull. By doing this she ensured his ability, later in life, to see the otherworld. Peggy of the red hair had high ambition for her son. She had foreseen that he would become the greatest seer in the whole of Scotland through the use of a seeing stone of unmatched power and she understood that her life's purpose was the furtherance of this vision of his greatness.

Rab Robertson, meanwhile, continued to carry his burden across the island, unaware of what awaited him. The tracks were poor and he was assailed by the cold rains of Lewis. He stumbled across moors and through bogs; he wandered lost through sudden mists. He was sustained only by the conviction that great wealth was due to be his. It took him several days to reach Loch Ceann Hulabhig, where he rested his pack on a rock. There Rab tasted the water and its faint saltiness told him he was at the head of a sea loch. He now knew there would be fishing villages ahead eager for his wares. Fortified by this happy expectation, he used his last strength to follow a track that led to a croft at Lundal. He found a small bothy with a roof that leaked but little. Gratefully he entered and fell into an exhausted sleep.

In the morning, what did he see on waking but a small girl standing wide-eyed in the doorway, watching him. He started to speak encouragingly to her but she ran off in fear, as strangers were few in these parts and she was startled. Soon she returned with her father. The pedlar was now faced with a difficult matter of judgment. He wanted to make a good impression, for ill news will always travel fast and, if the crofter was offended, a bad word could mean that none would buy his wares. Yet long experience had taught him that to give a gift to one crofter would create expectations in others and that he must protect the price of his goods. He made a swift decision. Rab reached into his pack and pulled out the stone. Using the alluring imagination that came readily to pedlars in general and to himself in the particular, he told the astonished girl, "This is a pebble of wondrous beauty that has come all the way from Loch Ussie, where it was long the pride of the Seaforth family." He little knew that his embellishment contained more truth than he intended.

He handed the stone to the small girl, who was delighted by the gift. Her father smiled and soon he and Rab were engaged in the exchanging of news and gossip that has ever made pedlars welcome in remote parts. While they talked, the child occupied herself threading rushes through the stone's hole to fashion a handle by which she could carry it. For the reward of some fishhooks from the pedlar's pack, the crofter agreed to row Rab Robertson across the straits of Loch Roag to the peninsula of Valtos and the jetty of Miavaig. From there he could cross the hills to Timsgarry and the scattered communities of Uig, where the crofter predicted there would be a market for his goods. Accordingly, the man and his daughter ferried the pedlar across and, after beaching the boat, walked with him in a companionable way up the hill above Glen Valtos, the girl trailing behind the men, dragging the stone precariously by its slender threading of rushes. At the top of the rise they parted and the pedlar from Inverness continued on alone. Before long he made out the figure of a handsome woman with long red hair climbing the hill as if to meet him.

The woman fixed her eyes on Rab and so intent was her gaze that he was held fast in his tracks as if bound by cords. As she reached him, she put her face close to his, forcing him back a pace. She held out a hand to the pedlar and her voice was urgent, "Give me the Stone you have brought, for it is destined for me." Rab Robertson, at first, could not understand what she meant. Peggy of the red hair told him she had the gift of seeing and had used her second sight to follow every movement of the Stone from Loch Ussie. To prove the truth of what she said, she recounted the terrible circumstances of the death of Glen Birrell. At this moment, Rab Robertson was seized by a chilling fear, knowing for the first time that great powers were at work beyond the Seer's prophecy which had guided his steps to this spot. Again, she held out her hand towards him and her eyes became cold and demanding.

The pedlar was apprehensive, fearing the power of this strange woman, and told her how he had unknowingly given the Stone to the child from Lundal just a short time since. Red Peggy shrieked a fearful cry and, turning on her heel, chased as fast as one of her goats, over the hill toward Miavaig where the crofter's boat was beached. She overtook the father and child just as they were readying the boat to push off from the shore. Rab climbed back to the crest of the hill and from there he watched Red Peggy on the beach below in earnest discourse with the crofter. The wind gusted and he could not hear their words. After a time all three started back up the hill, the two adults seeming to search the ground as they made their way.

When they reached the pedlar, the father told how, through the inadvertent carelessness of the young, the rush handle had unravelled and the child had dropped the Stone during their walking. They all traced and retraced their steps but the Stone was not to be found. The red-haired woman closed her eyes and gave out a long keening sound, entering a trance-like state. The others waited in awe until she reopened her eyes. She dismissed them, declaring that the Stone was hiding from her *sight* and could only be winkled from its place of concealment by some enchantment or by the use of a raven. Rab, having fulfilled his purpose so inadequately, was of no further use to *Peigi Ruadh* so she turned her back on him, lapsing again into a trance while she considered how she could recover the lost Stone. The pedlar from Inverness was glad to escape the strangeness of Red Peggy and so he bade her farewell and continued down the hill to Uig Bay.[10]

That night, when the moon was at its full, Peggy crept from her shieling to visit a raven's nest she had been watching. The night was cloudless, and the stars were sharp. Because ravens meet together in parliament on the sands of Uig Bay at the low tide of the full moon, she knew that tonight their nests would be unguarded. She made her stealthy way along the cliffs above the bay and saw, beneath her in the distance, darkly silvered ravens' backs as the birds strutted gravely in their discourse upon the whitened sands. Quickly she found the nest and stole from it the four eggs, taking them back in her apron and slipping them beneath the boiling water of a pot that hung above her fire. When the eggs were hard, she gathered them up again in her apron and returned silently to replace them in the nest before the raven returned. Peggy walked back along the beach and, as stealth was no longer required of her, she strode boldly across the rim of the moon-bleached sands, passing the pool at Baile na Cille. Her presence raised a clamour of cawing from the ravens, whose secret deliberations had been so discourteously interrupted by her.

Later that night the raven whose eggs Peggy had so transformed returned to her nest, seeing naught that was amiss. After seven days, when her eggs failed to hatch, she became unsettled and tipped them from the nest. Then she flew hither and yon, searching for replacements that she could hatch in the stead of her natural eggs. It is in the nature of ravens, engaged in such a hunt, to be attracted to seeing stones. It has long been known, among students of the otherworld, that there is no better way to find a good stone than to cause a raven to seek one. The raven searched for three days, considering and rejecting many stones, before swooping down into one of the peat banks that the child had crossed and rising with the Stone in its beak. Red Peggy's seeing sense was alerted by the bird's croak of triumph and she knew that the Stone would soon be in her own hands. With her possession of the Stone, she had foreseen great deeds and much fame for her son.

Peggy retrieved the Stone from the nest but had been forewarned by second sight that she must never herself raise it to her own eye. Instead, she placed the Stone in a pot that she filled with seawater. This she buried outside her shieling, covering the spot with a planting of bog violets to deter interfering spirits. The Stone would wait there for nigh-on twenty years before she would unearth it and give it to her son, Kenneth Odhar, so that he might go forth and make prophecies the like of which Scotland had never known before or since.

And then the Stone, having travelled so laboriously from Loch Ussie, would travel back there and the knot of time would weave itself into a circle where none could discern its beginning or know its end.

On the Nature of the Summer Walkers

Robert Heron, a chronicler much admired in his own day, journeyed through the western counties of Scotland and learned an admiration of the Summer Walkers and of them he wrote: *Chapmen or pedlars are the great civilizers of countries and nations. Nothing could be more natural than that this should so happen. A rude people will hardly go in search of commodities of which they know not the names, the nature or the value. Yet when such commodities are brought among them, exposed to their view and recommended as fashionable or useful, they seldom fail to take a fancy for them. They learn to disdain the use of those coarse clothes, or rude utensils with which they were before content. It is further to be observed for the credit of this most useful class of men that they commonly contribute by their personal manners no less than by the sale of their wares, to the refinement of the people among whom they travel. Their dealings form them to great quickness of wit, and acuteness of judgment. Having constant occasion to recommend themselves and their goods, they acquire habits of the most obliging attention and the most insinuating address. As they wander, each alone, through thinly inhabited districts, they form habits of reflection and of sublime contemplation. With all these qualifications, no wonder, that they should often be, in remote parts of the country, the best mirrors of fashion, and censors of manners; and should contribute much to polish the roughness and soften the rusticity of our peasantry.*

∞

A pedlar from Dundee had an enchanted tray, which he bought from a witch in Dunkeld for a high price. He used the tray to display his wares. The nature of the witch's spell ensured that any item of merchandise standing upon the tray, although it should be bought and locked away by its new owner, would, the next day, vanish and reappear in the pedlar's pack. By this black art it was the pedlar's intent to visit crofts and to sell the same item many times over and so enrich himself. In this he achieved great success as, in anticipation of selling the same goods again and again, he kept his prices favourable and he found ready buyers. Each day he sold all the items on the tray and moved off before the disappearance of his goods should be discovered. As the witch had promised, all the wares he sold returned the next day to his pack.

The pedlar had good reason to be satisfied with the enchanted tray. To his dismay, however, he found that every night the money he had taken for his previous day's labours was missing from his purse. Suspecting thievery, he counted his coin and tied his purse around his neck so that it could not be pilfered. Next day, the money he had earned from his commerce the day before was again gone. He was unable to apprehend the thief and soon the pedlar was in dire straits. When he returned impoverished to Dunkeld he implored the witch to take back the tray and restore to him his purchase money.

The witch laughed and told him that he had reaped the just reward of greed. She revealed to the disconsolate pedlar that her mother was a poor crofter's widow who had been cheated of all she had by a dishonest packman. In consequence of this she had made the spell so that on the very instant that one of his wares reappeared in the pedlar's pack, so would the money paid for it return into the crofter's purse.

∞

The life of pedlars and chapmen was ever hard, and never more difficult than in trafficking with the gentry. The chronicler Robert Heron relates that the itinerant merchants of Perth oft times found the Highland lairds more willing to buy than to pay.

A chapman who made a dunning visit on one of these gentlemen for the purpose of recovering his owings, was courteously received, and lodged for the night in a comfortable bed chamber. He was surprised when he rose in the morning, thinking to demand his money from the laird, to see opposite to his window the dead body of a man hanging upon a tree. He enquired concerning this appearance from the first servant who entered his chamber. The servant told him that this was the body of a merchant from the low country who had come to dun the laird for a debt he owed, and that the laird had, in a passion at the fellow's insolence, ordered him to be strung up. Upon receiving this information, the chapman resolved to take his leave of his host without mentioning the subject of his coming.

The laird was well pleased with the success of his trick; for he who hung on the tree was but a man of straw who had been dressed and put there, of purpose that his fate might terrify the real creditor from making a troublesome demand.

∞

The Summer Walkers, be they pedlars or pearl fishers, chapmen or cobblers, tinkers or the vendors of trinkets and trifles, are the heralds of summer for the Highlands and Islands as surely as the coming of swallows. Their number includes gypsies, fortune-tellers and horse dealers. They bring goods and they bring gossip. They leave behind them tales for the retelling and wares that proudly adorn every croft where last year's harvest was good enough to provide a surplus sufficient to buy a modicum of luxury. When they leave, it has been known for sheep to disappear mysteriously.

∞

Among the Summer Walkers, the Black Tinkers, *Ceardannan* in the old tongue, are a debased and unfortunate people. They are the heirs to a high caste of Celtic masters of metalcraft and it is said of them that they have so fallen that they have become 'the fluxion of the ages'. Where once they worked in silver and gold, they now employ only lead and tin. From the fashioning of fine swords that became the proud heirlooms of the noblest in the land, they are reduced to patching pots. Yet pride still stirs in their blood and when they speak the Travellers' tongue, they have the musical inflection of times long past and the tales they tell are beyond compare.

A Rhyme, a Riddle and a Secret

THE PRINCESS GRADHAG WAS CONTENTED. It was a fine spring afternoon and the world was as light as her heart. She had become an authority; a power in her father's land, and her *seeings* had proved both exact and fortunate. The five great ships of Lochlin had been sent out in accordance with her advice and had prospered in their raiding, ensuring that the King's coffers were filling. Her father regarded her well. As she lowered the Stone from her eye she felt the stirrings of a new excitement. The Stone had this very day given her a new foresight of a rich treasure and she sensed that the piles of gold she had seen were destined for Lochlin. The Princess knew the Stone well by now. It played a lovers' game with her, offering a mere glimpse then tantalising her curiosity by refusing to reveal more. Gradhag had learned, if she feigned indifference, that the Stone would tempt her with a more detailed sight. So she contained the exhilaration within her and waited.

For many days, as she prepared to use the Stone for her workaday predictions of fortunate marriage or good fishing, Gradhag sought to rid her mind of thoughts of the treasures she had seen. She knew well that the Stone sensed her interest and would withhold sight if she let inquisitiveness take hold of her. The Princess was about to lower the Stone after a foretelling when she saw, out of the corner of her eye, another glimpse of gold. She looked but pretended not to look. The Stone rewarded her with a full sighting. Now Gradhag saw a bulky ship. It was hiding in a narrow sea loch, marked by a black rock at the seaward entrance in the shape of a seal with a bulging collar at its neck. The ship carried a cargo of richly wrought gold and precious stones. It was heavily laden, waiting for good weather and for armed vessels from Ireland, which had been dispatched to guard it on its journey home. There were few sailors aboard and they spoke in an unfamiliar tongue. The young Princess had heard such speech before, however, and knew it to be the Irish royal dialect. Fascinated, she watched as men from her father's ships overwhelmed the crew and loaded sack after plundered sack into the Lochlin ships.

Without delay Gradhag urged her father to ready the ships of Lochlin for a great raid. Later that day the Stone was yet more forthcoming and revealed to her three scenes. First, it showed four Irish ships in pursuit as the Lochlin raiders fled across the Minch with their plunder. Next, it showed the Princess herself, standing on the deck of her father's flagship, besting the Blue Men of the Minch in a riddling contest. Finally, the Stone showed her a great storm with no sign of the Irish vessels other than four piles of wreckage on the sands. Every time Gradhag held the Stone to her eye she saw these exact scenes repeated. The meaning was clear. She must herself go with the raiders to aid them in defeating the Blue Men. After the Irish fleet was wrecked she would return to Lochlin to an honoured place in the history of her father's Kingdom.

The King, when he heard her plan, feared for his daughter's safety and tried to dissuade her from her risky purpose, but Gradhag was determined. She had seen that she alone could best the Blue Men in a rhyming contest; there was no other choice. Realising that he would not deflect her intention, the King called his astrologer, Gundur the Shrewd, and instructed the sage to protect Gradhag by any means he could. Gundur gave her an amulet set with enchanted runes and offered her secret charms to hide about her person. Most of these charms, such as yew sprigs and willow shavings, she instructed her maids to sew into the hem of her outer garments. But there was one thing he gave her that stood out from the rest. It was a ring with runes engraved upon it and set into it was a small red jewel in the shape of a seal. The ring stirred some memory in the Princess but she could not recognise why it seemed familiar. Gundur the Shrewd also created for her a neckpiece, with a leather pouch attached, to hold the Stone safely around her neck. He had correctly divined that her destiny and the destiny of the Stone were linked and not to be separated. The neckpiece featured intricate plaitwork and there was much enchantment in it that the eye could not discern. It had been crafted from the skin of a ewe, but not any ewe. It had been tanned, but not as ordinary skins were tanned. It held great magic.

That night the Stone whispered to Gradhag over and over again as she slept. When she awoke, she had the rhymes of the Blue Men embedded in her memory and she knew how they must be answered. She met her father's sea captains in the morning and described to them the harbour she had seen, where the treasure ship lay at anchor. As she spoke of the rock in the shape of a collared seal, the captains looked knowingly at one another. They could discern at once, from the seal rock and from other particulars of what they had heard, that the ship was hidden within an inlet on the north-west coast of the Isle of Skye. Until that moment, Gradhag had not been able to understand why the ring had seemed so familiar. Now it came to her. The shape of the ring's stone was an exact miniature of the seal rock guarding the harbour. She took this as a fine omen and placed the ring securely in the leather pouch with the Stone.

Soon all was ready. Her father came to bid her farewell and, as a token of great esteem, he presented her with a silver key whose head was an intricately fashioned Celtic knot. "This key signifies that you hold the key to my kingdom," he told her, "for if you succeed in this enterprise you will make Lochlin wealthy above all our rivals."

"I shall treasure this gift," replied Gradhag, putting the key into the pouch around her neck, "and when I return I shall use my Stone to unlock even greater treasure for you."

The ships rowed from the shelter of their moorings and hoisted sail. The captains predicted an easy journey as their raiding fleet set forth. And so it proved, with fast and favourable winds to speed their passage. The seizure of the treasure was effortless beyond their imagining, with feeble resistance from the small Irish crew. The Lochlin ships began their return home across the Minch joyfully, thinking themselves great conquerors protected by invulnerable magic. Even the common sailors, long accustomed to the reversals of the sea and ever given to suspicion and caution, spoke of good omens. They had captured treasure beyond their dreaming. The King would take the greatest part, then those of noble birth, then the sea captains and after that the master mariners. But with such an unimagined excess of wealth, there would surely be bounty for all. Never, they told each other, never in all the annals of the sea, had so much been gained with such ease.

The Princess Gradhag held back her satisfaction because she alone knew that the most hazardous moments of the enterprise were yet to come. She stood on the foredeck of the flagship, the Stone held around her neck in the pouch, where it nestled with the ring and the key. She watched the colours of the Minch shift and change under the keel, as the waters are wont to do when the Blue Men begin to weave a storm-knot beneath the waves. The sea captain whispered to her that the Blue Men were near. Suddenly the wind died and the little fleet was becalmed, though the waves swelled and the Minch swirled angrily around the stout ships. Ahead of them a Blue Man emerged from the sea, floating waist deep on the shifting waters. He called to them in the old tongue, saying that a sea-knot was woven around them and in its coils they must die. The Princess shouted back the challenge to a rhyming, knowing that the Blue Men are powerless to resist such a contest.

Nevertheless, the Blue Man at first spurned her call, insisting that only the captain of a vessel might engage in a rhyming contest. The captain of the flagship stepped forward, declaring that he, and the other captains, were but underlings to the Princess, who was of royal blood. This satisfied the Blue Man who, exactly as the Stone had foreseen, swung himself up onto the bow of the flagship and perched there, dripping and marvellous. He regarded the Princess with the greatest curiosity for a long moment. Then, in a high singing voice, like the wind through rigging, he chanted: "My brothers and I shall let you safely through our sea, if you can best us in rhymes three. My first contest a rhyme alone shall be. Then to my brother, if you best me, a rhyme and a riddle will come readily. And should you answer cunningly, then you must face the brother three. From him a rhyme, a riddle and a mystery. If you guess our secret you are free."

The Princess accepted the challenge and the Blue Man began the first rhyme:

Show me why I'd spare your boat,
You that dwell on land not sea.

Using exactly the words the Stone had shown her, Gradhag replied in the old tongue:

You ken full well I'll stay afloat
For I can rhyme as deft as thee.

The Blue Man uttered loud curses and, slipping from the bow, disappeared beneath the waves. The waters of the Minch roiled fearfully and a second Blue Man emerged. He was larger than his

105

brother and there were streaks of red in his hair like summer kelp. "To the rhyme and the riddle together," he said, climbing onto the foredeck. In a mighty voice, like the flapping of a huge sail, he called out:

It has a skin it will not show
Except in moonlight once each year.

Gradhag shouted back the Stone's response:

The selkies shed their pelt I know
And dance uncloth'd when none are near.

The second Blue Man gave her a look of terrible malice but, knowing his rhyme and riddle were both fully answered, he too returned to the sea and the Minch closed above his head. Finally, the water before the ships erupted into a boiling whirlpool. From its depths came the eldest brother. He was a giant and when he climbed aboard the ship was weighed down nigh to sinking.[11] His hair was shaggy and the colour of winter storm clouds. In a thunderous voice, like a great ship splintering upon rocks, he roared: "You made a rhyme as bid; a rhyme and a riddle you did. Now for the secret we have hid." The timbers of the stout ship shook as he called out the Blue Men's final challenge:

Tis blue, tis grey, tis white, tis green
And made in secret 'neath the sea.

The Princess, using all her strength, shouted back without hesitation, answering the rhyme, the riddle and the mystery:

You weave a water-knot unseen
My Stone betrays your tricks to me.

Realising that the foresight of the Stone had cheated them of their prize, the giant Blue Man uttered a terrible cry of rage. He leapt back into the whirlpool and was gone. As he sank he called out a vow to be avenged on the next ships to enter the Minch. In an instant the sea became calm and a gentle breeze sprang up. The sailors cheered and counted themselves truly blessed to have in their midst a seer so great that she could defy the Blue Men, whom all sailors fear. They continued across the Minch, making fair and prosperous progress. The sea captains set the sharpest eyes amongst them to look astern, for Gradhag had foreseen that four Irish ships would pursue them. They had scant worry, however, for they had heard the Blue Man's vow to wreck the next vessels to cross the threshold of the Minch and so they jested that the Blue Men would do their fighting for them.

As they left the Minch behind them, great shouts of triumph and relief rose from the Lochlin ships. They had the treasure, they had bested the Blue Men and they knew themselves to be faster than the enemy behind them. Nothing, now, could stand between them and home. Their cheers had scarce died when four well-armed Irish ships of war appeared from the north, ahead of them, blocking their homeward course. This threw the Lochlin sea captains into great confusion. All had understood that the warships would come to pursue them from the Isle of Skye, to the south. None had imagined that the Irish would sail up the west coast of Lewis and, while the Lochlin ships were riddling with the Blue Men in the Minch, make sufficient way to cut them off.

The captains had no choice left them. They went about and headed back into the Minch. At first their stratagem thrived. Their ships were fast and they outran the Irish. The sea was wild but their four ships were of sturdy design and they weathered the waves of the Minch with ease. But it is in the nature of fate to grant an appearance of safety to those who are marked for death. The Lochlin ships were a hair's breadth from safe haven when the three Blue Men appeared to block their escape. The Blue Men had made a vow to wreck the next ships to enter their waters and the Lochlin vessels were now their quarry. Nor would they countenance a rhyming contest, for the last one – in their judgment – was won by the trickery of foresight and not by the skill of the moment. They had woven a mighty storm-knot from the multi-hued waters of the Minch and this they unleashed upon the fleet from Lochlin. The ships were strong and their captains skilled but, as the seas rose, the waves would seem to grow higher than the hills of Harris. The fury of the Blue Men was beyond belief. For the remainder of that day and all the following night the fleet was driven south by the vast storm. They hoped for respite by heading around the island, as the Irish ships had done. To lighten the ships, all was thrown overboard and, in the last extremity, the crew even cast the golden treasures into the sea, hoping to placate the Blue Men. But nothing could prevail against the storm, which now drove them north along the west coast of Lewis with ever increasing ferocity. Off their starboard bow they could see, looming before them, Gallan Head and the jagged rocks of the Uig coastline. Their ships were driven relentlessly and, in that moment, all aboard knew that they were doomed.

Gripping the rail with one hand, Princess Gradhag lifted the Stone to her eye in a final and forlorn hope that she might yet see safety. Her own perfect reflection stared back up at her from beneath the calm water of a pool, her pale face unmoving and her loosened fair hair wafting and eddying like kelp to the waves.

On the Nature of the Blue Men of the Minch

The Blue Men of the Minch have long accosted sailors who traverse the northern seas, often with unfortunate consequences befalling those who meet them. Some say that Blue Men and storm kelpies are one and the same, for they are both man-like creatures of the sea, blue of skin, who ride the storms to torment sailors. Others, relying on credible observation by mariners of many nations, believe that storm kelpies roam further afield and are more inclined towards mischief than malice. The Blue Men, who weave great storm-knots in the water, rarely stray beyond the Minch, although they have been sighted as far off as Norway, sometimes in the company of selkies.

∞

The annals recount how the Blue Men, who are of the sea, came to the Minch when the fallen angels were banished forever from Paradise. After their banishment, the fallen angels divided into three clans, the Fairies, the White Men and the Blue Men. The Fairies are of the earth; they dwell in and under the land and are spread throughout all parts where the old tongues are spoken. The White Men are variously called the Nimble Men, the Merry Dancers or the Sky Streamers and they are of the sky. They dwell only in the northern skies where, on certain nights in the spring and autumn, they dance to create the *aurora borealis*.

∞

All three of the clans are capricious and, by knowing their fancies, they can be controlled or diverted from their malevolent or fickle intents. The Fairies have a weakness for music and many have escaped from their bonds by lulling them with song. The Nimble Men are entranced by dancing and the Blue Men are held by the power of rhyme. When a chosen ship approaches, a clan chief of the Blue Men rises from the waters of the Minch and calls out a riddle in the form of a rhyme. If the captain answers with a well-rhymed response, his ship is allowed to pass unharmed. A sea captain must be armed with a ready wit and the knack of a quick rhyme if he is to safely sail the Minch.

∞

The Blue Men are thought to use a massive seeing stone to foretell when ships will pass. Long ago they possessed a stone of legendary power but this was taken from them by the trickery of sailors. Their eternal vengeance remains the sinking of ships.

∞

Blue Men are most particularly found within the Minch in the channel between the Isle of Lewis and the Charmed Isles, known as the Shiants. This strait – called in the Gaelic *Sruth nam Fir Gorm*, The Stream of the Blue Men or The Current of Destruction – is treacherous and many a stout ship has foundered there. The clan of the Blue Men, and their king, dwell in submarine caves in the depths of the strait. Kings of the Blue Men are crowned there in an undersea cathedral made of green ice. So vast is this cathedral that it chills the waters that surround it, which is why the Stream of the Blue Men is the coldest sea in all the islands.

∞

Although the Blue Men will respond to rhymes or riddles posed in several tongues, they have a predilection for the Old Norse. A single stanza declaimed in the high skaldic manner of the Icelandic bards will cause the Blue Men to concede in any rhyming contest.

∞

It is said that their deference to this form results from a contest with the great Icelandic bard Egill Skallagrímsson himself, who created the great *Egil's Saga*, believed by many to be the finest of all the sagas. Skallagrímsson was both a poet and a pirate, loved and feared throughout Iceland. He was singularly ugly and uncouth in his appearance, so that few took him to be the greatest poet of his age.

He was crossing the Minch while returning to Iceland from Ireland, where he had been engaged in a brawl with sundry Irish bards. Upon being challenged to a rhyming contest by the Blue Men, he behaved scornfully towards them, saying that it would be unfair for him to match rhymes with them, due to his superior skill. The Blue Men were enraged and swore they would sink his boat unless he could sustain a high rhyme for a whole hour. This would be an unparalleled feat, for the complexity of the high style meant that a single extemporized stanza was a notable achievement.

Egill Skallagrímsson sustained the rhyme to perfection for three hours and, in addition, gave a stress to three syllables in each line and left the last unstressed, which is considered the summit of the rhymer's art. In recognition of this great achievement, the Blue Men concede defeat whenever their opponents can declaim even a single stanza in the high skaldic style.

∞

In times past at Hallowtide, the sailors and crofters of the Outer Isles went to the shores of the Minch to light candles. There they poured a firkin of new ale into the water, to propitiate the Blue Men, who were known to have a partiality for such things. In this ceremony, before the candles were extinguished, the crofters entreated the Blue Men to leave kelp on the beach to enrich their thin soil. The sailors sought safe passage across the treacherous waters.

∞

The Blue Men have webbed feet of a curious shape. A similarity of shape and webbing can be seen in the feet of the men of St Kilda, who live by climbing the crags and cliffs of their island, leading many to suppose that there has been some mixing of bloods in times past. It is of equal plausibility that the men of St Kilda have merman or selkie blood in their line.

∞

William Nicolson was a proud sea captain of great renown. He once navigated safely through the great whirlpool of Lochlin and was famed for his daring seamanship.

He was admired by all who knew the ways of the sea. Yet he was in great fear of the Blue Men, believing that in a time past one of his family had given some offence to them. In consequence of this, for many years, he avoided all crossing of the Minch until the day came when he could defer no longer. Knowing that a rhyme would be demanded for his life he was perplexed, for he had not the skill of rhyming.

As he sat on the harbour wall at Mallaig, unhappily pondering the certitude of his undoing, he was hailed by Fingal of Achintore, a bard of some accomplishment, who wished passage to the Outer Isles. Acting upon a sudden apprehension of good fortune, the captain promised safe passage if the bard would become captain for the voyage, to which the poet gave his agreement. Captain Nicolson drew up a paper to that accord, making Fingal captain for the duration of the crossing of the Minch.

As they drew into the strait between the Shiants and Lewis, three Blue Men arose from the sea and called out, demanding to know which among the crew was Captain Nicolson. William Nicolson replied that, although he once bore that title, he was no longer master of the ship. This flung the Blue Men into great confusion, for they possessed a seeing stone which had foreseen that they would out-rhyme the master of the ship, a Captain Nicolson, and would exact a sinking as the penalty. There was earnest debate amongst them on what course to take. Finally the keeping of custom prevailed over the seeing of the stone. On being shown the paper as proof that Fingal of Achintore was indeed the new master, the Blue Men engaged him in a rhyming contest. Fingal bested them with ease and the Blue Men had no choice but to release the ship.

∞

Although a safe crossing is assured by besting the Blue Men in a rhyming contest, there are other means by which seamen have escaped them. One vessel was carrying kegs of rare whisky in its cargo when it was stopped at sea by a band of Blue Men. The captain remarked to them that it would be a great misfortune if these kegs were to be wasted and proposed opening a single keg and drinking from it one toast to the art of rhyming ere the contest should begin.

The Blue Men were cautious, yet such was their dedication to rhyming that they could not refuse the toast. One toast became many and one keg became two, until the Blue Men fell asleep and slid back beneath the waves. The captain was able to cross safely but, when he reached harbour, there were those among the merchants waiting to receive his cargo who expressed little satisfaction with a tale in which two missing kegs provided the sole evidence for the truth of these singular events.

∞

It is not known how the Blue Men choose which ships to challenge and which to let pass unhindered. It has long been told in taverns, most particularly by those whose utterances owe more to liquor than to learning, that there are certain feast days safe from attack. Though widely repeated by common sailors, most scholars of repute dispute the veracity of this belief.

∞

It was, at one time, widely believed that the Blue Men appeared only to one ship in each hundred, letting the other ninety-nine pass unmolested. The origin of this belief was a pedlar from the mainland who had come to Lewis to sell his wares. When his load of fishhooks and clothes-pegs had been profitably disposed of, he returned from Uig to the port of Stornoway but hesitated to make his way home across the Minch. He supposed that ill-luck might be upon him, as he had inadvertently carried a malicious seeing stone from Loch Ussie in his pack.

It had been told him by a red-headed woman with second sight that the Stone had brought death to many and would bring death to more. In consequence of his fear, he closely watched all vessels arriving or departing across the Minch, writing details in a black book. It was his hope that he might discern a pattern from his observations, whether by time of day, date or some other cause, which would show him when a crossing would be safest.

The activities of strangers have ever aroused suspicion and curiosity among island folk and soon the whole town of Stornoway was talking of him. Captains came to consult him for advice on when to cross and the pedlar found they would pay well for his counsel. In time he built a thriving trade and became wealthy from his prognostications. It was he who put forward the proposition that the Blue Men kept a counting, using a pile of one hundred pebbles. Every time their watchmen saw a vessel pass over their heads, they moved one pebble from the pile. When only a single pebble of the hundred remained, they would weave a sea-knot from all the hues of the waters to destroy the next ship to cross.

After many years, and having amassed great riches, the pedlar desired to return to his home in Inverness. A ship had been sunk in the Minch and it was supposed that it was the work of the Blue Men. The pedlar counted the next fifty vessels to cross and reasoned that this was the point of greatest safety. He chartered a large ship, loaded it with his worldly goods and set off across the Minch for home. No sooner had his ship entered the strait than a mighty army of Blue Men appeared and dragged the pedlar to his doom, together with all his wealth. As a consequence of his ill fortune, his theories fell into immediate disrepute and died with him. But, even today, he has some defenders who say that it was the Stone, not an erroneous proposition, that was the cause of his doom.

The Dry Well

THERE HAVE BEEN DIFFERING ACCOUNTS concerning the temperament and character of Kenneth Odhar, the Seer of Brahan. Some speak of him as dour and dull in nature, taciturn to a fault. Others have averred him to be a man of learning and of ready wit. In certain tellings his caustic tongue was his downfall, but other accounts declare that he ever had a soft answer. By turns, he was called subtle and he was called gross; a man of peace and a belligerent. The manifest contradictions concerning his character have left many things unexplained. Commonly, the Seer's chroniclers have chosen whichever temperament best appeals to the tenor of their tale, with little regard for fact or history. The possibility cannot be denied that all are correct, for the Seer appears, and was credibly accounted for, in different ages that are centuries apart from each other. No life of single mortal man could span these countless years. It was widely supposed that, due to his birth near Baile na Cille, where the knot of time reverses, he crossed into ages that were not naturally his own. In consequence of this he lived multiple lives and, in each life, may have been possessed of differences in character and circumstances. Where does truth lie?

In olden times, both the spinner of a tale and the listener had a ready acceptance that all things, however constant they might appear, may have been transmuted; a giant one day might readily transform into a dwarf the next; a pauper to a prince or a selkie into a woman. In the high years of the bards and the great hewers of northern legends, the seeming contradictions within the Brahan Seer's life would be embraced as rich ornament, not interpreted as confusion. The bards would relish the tale of Kenneth Odhar for the infinite creations that coil from its twisted strands. One of these strands is told here, but we shall meet others that counter each twist and deny each turn of this telling.

This account of Kenneth Odhar commenced on the Seaforth lands in Lewis, where there was a lad called *Coinneach a Gaothach,* Kennie the Wind. Amongst all the boys of the estate, none was so fleet of foot as he. He was scarce into his eighth year, yet over rough ground already he outpaced most men. It was not that he could outrun a nimble man along a smooth cart track or on the wide sands of Uig, for on level ground it is a long stride that confers speed and distance. Kennie the Wind's swiftness was because he was endowed with a capacity to move without effort or thought across the rough Hebridean landscape. This, said the other boys, was in consequence of his *seeing* feet. Over rain-slick rocks, through the tufted pastures and bogs, he kept a sure footing, never slowing and never the once looking down. "His mother has the second sight," they jested, "but Kennie has it only in his toes." His agility soon had him running errands on the estate. Lord Kenneth Mor MacKenzie, third Earl of Seaforth, was Laird of Kintail and of the Seaforth estates. When he visited his lands it was young Kennie the Wind who chased to the stables with a message requiring new horses to be sent for the Laird and it was young Kennie who brought news to the kitchen that the hunters were returning.

The Laird of Kintail took an interest in the lad, finding the boy answered well and was possessed of a ready wit. When the time arrived to return to Brahan Castle and to the mainland estates, the

Laird spoke with Angus MacLeod his factor, revealing his interest in taking the boy back with him. The Reverend Farquhar MacRae, Minister of Kintail, had established at Eilean Donan Castle a seminary for the children of gentlemen and for common children of promise and upright character. Kenneth Mor MacKenzie himself was enrolled there as a child and had learned well. He was of the belief that young Kennie the Wind would derive enduring benefit from such education and, in turn, would offer greater value to the Seaforth estate. Acting on his master's instructions, MacLeod made a promise to seek the consent of the boy's mother, although he warned that she had the second sight and was, by reputation, intransigent to the will of others. Next day he returned to the Laird and told him of all that had transpired from his meeting with the mother of Kennie the Wind. To the factor's wonderment, as he explained to the Earl, the woman had revealed that her son was under a curse from a seeing stone. If this curse were to be fulfilled it would be his death, to forestall the which she had hidden the Stone where it would not be found. Nevertheless, she feared the Stone's power, the more particularly because she had it from a dead princess, who had made the adverse predictions that affected her son. She would wish for nothing better than to get young Kennie safely away from Lewis. Accordingly, Angus MacLeod reported, she had given her blessing in the hope that her son would remain forever upon the mainland. The mother placed but a single condition upon the arrangement: that neither the factor nor the Laird would reveal to the lad that he lay under mortal threat from a hidden stone.

In furtherance of this agreement, young Kennie returned with the Laird to Brahan castle and there he was introduced to the Reverend Farquhar MacRae. The preacher was visiting Kintail, where he had the living of the parish. MacRae agreed to take the boy with him back to the seminary at Eilean Donan Castle. At first the other pupils there teased Kennie beyond endurance, as boys are wont to do when an unfamiliar lad is placed in their midst, for he stared strangely and his clothing was threadbare. Some called him 'the island savage', and made great mockery of his uncouth ways. In time, however, he gained admiration from the other boys, first for his fleet footing and then for his quick wit. Within a term Kennie the Wind was his name to all and he was well accepted by his fellows.

The Reverend Farquhar MacRae was less sanguine concerning the boy's scholarly progress. Kennie was inattentive in the classroom and showed meagre interest in learning. He oftentimes stared at things that others could not see; his eyes fixing on emptiness and then intently following the track of some invisible creature that had life only in his imagination. He responded to voices that he alone could hear, and in the doing so distracted the other boys from memorising their scriptures. Kennie had a trick of knowing when visitors would come, and announced their names and impending arrival even before their intention to visit had become known to MacRae himself. The other boys regarded this with amusement, the more because the preacher was clearly disconcerted whenever Kennie declared that the seminary was about to receive an unexpected visit from a person of importance. There were whispers he had the second sight. It was evident to his teachers that the disturbance the boy caused to the regulated good order of the seminary required that Kennie should soon leave Eilean Donan Castle.

When summer came the seminary pupils departed; the rich to their ancestral estates, the common children to work the harvest on their family farms and crofts. The Reverend Farquhar MacRae took Kennie to Kintail and from thence delivered him to Brahan Castle. When Mor MacKenzie heard of the nature of the boy's conduct, the Laird concurred that Kennie should not return to Eilean Donan Castle after the harvest. He was, instead, put to work on the Brahan estate, where soon he showed great prowess with the spade. Whether it was in the digging of peats, or in the widening of a ditch, he had a knack that few could match. As he grew older and stronger, so did his spadework advance. Over the years, his fame spread and some now called him Kennie the Spade. People came from afar to watch him and marvelled at his speed and grace. There was a well-digging contest at the Inverness fair, where diggers from rival estates competed to be the first to quarry down to a depth of eight feet. Kennie reached the mark before his rivals were even halfway. The Laird was well pleased with this performance and, forgetful of the warning that Kennie's mother had given, took the young man with him when, in the spring following, he next visited his estates on Lewis.

The Laird's factor welcomed Kennie warmly and soon put him to work with the spade. He had heard of the young man's feats at the Inverness fair and remarked that there was a well near Baile na Cille that was in need of redigging. Kennie took this as a providential occurrence, for it allowed him to show his skill and also to visit his mother, whom he had not seen for the ten long years he had sojourned at Brahan. He shouldered his spade and trudged across the island until he reached Baile na Cille. There, Kennie learned that his mother was in Harris and was not expected to return for several weeks. He visited the dry well, called *Tobair na Circe*, the Well of the Church. The well was ancient, so old that the church for which it was named had long since sunk back into the peat and rocks of Lewis, leaving as its memorial only a grassy mound and desolate fragments of a wall. Kennie looked the well over and saw that it was indeed dry and partly filled with sand. He resolved to come the next day to dig it out and turned towards Uig to reacquaint himself with the friends of his childhood.

On his way down to the sands, an old shepherd appeared, as if from nowhere. On a whim, Kennie asked the man what he knew of the well at *Tobair na Circe*, for though he had a distant memory of it from his childhood, he understood nothing of its history or nature. The shepherd told him that the well had the sweetest water in all Lewis and that it was an enchanted well that cured the dropsy. It became dry after goats soiled it, for it was commonly known that enchanted wells have a temperament that abhors disrespect. He said darkly that Kennie's mother was the cause of the well's anger and warned him not to dig there. "Tell your mother," he said, "that, when her goats strayed at *Tobair na Circe,* she permitted a terrible insult and the people will ever suffer for it. Tell her of my words tomorrow night when she returns – aye, tell her of me. And yourself beware, for digging of that well will prove your undoing." Then the man was gone, his departure being as sudden and noiseless as his appearance.

When he reached Timsgarry, Kennie sought out his friend Iain Macaulay, the blacksmith's son. After they had reacquainted themselves with each other, Kennie told him of his strange meeting with the old shepherd. Iain Macaulay feared that the shepherd was a *Sithche,* a slinky one from the otherworld, and that his appearance was an ill omen. He urged his friend not to dig next day at the well. But Kennie had adopted the mainlanders' disregard for the customs and lore of the islands. He told Iain that he feared no superstitious apparition and added that the shepherd's misapprehension that his mother would return the following night, when all hereabouts knew full well that she would be away for weeks, was proof indeed that the old man's warning was equally mistaken.

The next day Kennie returned to *Tobair na Circe* to begin work on the well. The sand was loose and it cleared fast. Soon he reached an obdurate sediment, finding within its black heaviness a quantity of coins and charms. He knew these to have been thrown into the well for luck and supposed, from the number of silver coins, that at one time christenings took place here. He was respectful of everything he found and put each object he uncovered into a small pile, intending to return them all to the well after his digging was completed. When he reached a depth where his long spade could no longer throw earth clear of the well lip, he decided to cease for the day and to return the next morning with ladder, rope and creel.

He was readying himself to climb from the well when he saw two curious pebbles at his feet. Kennie carried them up with him and cleaned them off, the better to inspect them. The first pebble was white and perforated by a round hole. The second was blue and polished smooth, although it lacked a hole. Both stones had faint rune-like markings on them. When he held the white stone in his hand it felt familiar and he had a sudden vision of himself, long ago, pocketing just such a pebble at Baile na Cille on the sands of Uig. In consequence of this momentary image, he placed the white pebble in his pouch, reasoning that the meaning of the vision must be that the pebble was intended for him. He added the blue pebble to the pile of coins and charms that he had carefully amassed, with the intention of returning them to the well the next day.

That night Kennie went to his mother's summer shieling, meaning to sleep there. He was on the very edge of slumber when a noise from without disturbed him. Before he could begin to gather his wits, the door opened and in burst his mother, dishevelled and distressed. "Is it that I have come too late?" she panted. "I *saw* the danger and I have returned in hope of its prevention." Kennie could not comprehend her agitation. "Nothing has happened here amiss," he began. Then, on the sudden, he recalled how the *Sithche,* the shepherd from the otherworld, had told him his mother would return this night and how, to his friend, he had made scorn of the shepherd's words. He told his mother, "I dug the well at *Tobair na Circe* today but there was no happening of ill consequence."

"What was that thing you found there?" his mother demanded, her eyes staring into his very soul.

"Some coins and trinkets," he replied, "and all waiting to be returned safely to the well after my labours."

"So you took nothing?"

"Naught but this wee pebble," said Kennie, pulling the white Stone from his pouch. When she saw the Stone, his mother started back as one who had seen death. She uttered a lengthy and piercing wail, tearing at her long tresses of red hair. Her face turned white and her whole person shook as if afflicted by the plague. Then she fell silent and remained still for so long that Kennie feared she might be dead. He was about to shake her when she opened her eyes and, in a terrible whisper, told him a tale.

"I shall reveal all to you," she said. "When your father was snatched from us by the hand of death, you were scarce stirring in my belly. As was the custom of the time, for a month I stood watch each night over his grave at Baile na Cille, so that witches might not steal his body's parts to aid the power of their incantations. I took with me my collie dog that ran the herd with me, and I was grateful of its company, for every night the vigil was arduous and fearful. Each midnight, graves opened and the spirits flew from them, scattering far and wide but returning at the hour before cockcrow. The spirit of a young girl was ever the last to return and the collie took to lying on her grave. The girl's spirit entreated me to keep the collie away as no ghost may cross a living creature, be that creature man or beast, during its homecoming to the grave. In return I asked her why it was that she was so late. She replied that she was the daughter of an Irish king and had died of fever whilst on board ship. It had been intended for her to marry a prince from the Isle of Skye, whence the ship was bound, laden with a rich dowry of gold and jewels. On her death, the sailors had brought her body ashore and hastily buried it here, their fear of pirates and raiders making them apprehensive for the safety of their treasure. She now was the last to return to the grave because it was her land that was the furthest off."

Kennie was bemused by what he was hearing and could not guess the intent of his mother's tale. He stayed silent, transfixed, as she continued with her narrative.

"On hearing her sad recital, I kept the collie from the grave and for this she professed herself to be ever in my debt. When the month was up, she bade me farewell and, in the parting, offered me a gift for my unborn son, warning that he must not have the gift until he was a man. She told me to pick a pebble from her grave. I bent down and pulled from the soil a white stone that had a hole through it. She told me that you, my son, would have luck if this stone was employed wisely for the benefit of others and she prophesied that you would use the stone to help a red-headed woman. Then, on a sudden, I saw a look of terror come across the spirit's face. 'What have I done?' she whispered, 'I had intended good but now I foresee great harm, for though I see that he shall aid a red-headed woman, I now know that the same woman will repay him with death.' In distress the spirit enjoined me to pick a second pebble. This I did, finding a smooth blue stone. The spirit then spoke this prophecy: 'Although I cannot mitigate what I have seen, I can offer you some hope. When your son comes of age he will pick one of these two stones and put it in his pocket. Should he choose the blue stone, his life will be contented. The white stone will lead to his certain death. The spirit sank into the earth and next day I cast both stones into the well at *Tobair na Circe*, where no further enchantment could reach them, in the hope that her prophecy could be subverted."

Kennie was silent with shock as he listened to his mother's tale. "It was a mere pebble. Can I not throw it back into the well from whence I picked it?" he asked.

"You are too late," she lamented, "for, in the pocketing of it, you have its possession and your fate cannot be so simply denied."

The frantic woman paced back and forth as she considered what was best. "It may be," she confessed, "that I myself am that fatal woman, for none in these parts has hair as red as mine. Many times have I lain awake at night with the fear that, in the unfolding of fate, I would be my own son's undoing. My counsel is that you should leave here and return with your Laird to Brahan. Use the pebble as your instinct will advise you, being watchful that you do only good by its use. In this way you will complete the beneficial element of the prophecy and will prosper. Ever shun the company of red-headed women and, by such avoidance, it is my hope that you may still circumvent the fate predicted for you."

Kennie heeded his mother's words and returned to the mainland with the Laird, reaching Brahan castle within the week. There he made a purse of ewe leather and into this he placed the white pebble for safe keeping. He had no knowledge of how the Stone might be used, whether for good or for ill, and heartily wished it were not in his possession.

Soon, events of high drama drove all thought of the Stone from his mind. On the orders of General Monk, Kenneth Mor MacKenzie was arrested and taken to Inverness, where he was held on suspicion of insurrection and treason. During his incarceration there was great uncertainty and unease at Brahan, for none knew either the when or the whether of their Laird's return.

After upward of a year, word reached the castle by messenger that the Earl of Seaforth was released, and told of his impending return. He would bring home with him a new bride, the daughter of Lord Tarbat. Her name, said the messenger, was Isabella. The families of the estate assembled to greet their Laird and his lady, although the weather was inclement and they were compelled to stand shivering through the winter squalls and gusts. Despite the miserable wait, there was a hearty cheer as the Earl emerged from his coach into the driving rain. His bride Isabella followed after, swathed in a hooded black cloak for protection from the stormy night sky. As she neared Kennie, she looked at him intently and her eyes locked with his. She stumbled and he moved forward by instinct to help her, but she recovered her balance. The cloak hood slipped from her head revealing, in the lamplight, tresses of long red hair.

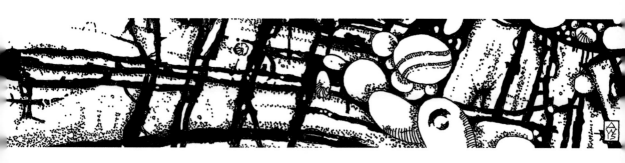

On the Nature of Wells

There is scarce a well on the islands of the Hebrides but has some power of healing and it is a testament to the efficacy of these wells that the health of island people is robust. Certain wells, such as *Tobar Mor*, the great well on the island of Gigha, are preventative or even curative of all disease. Others have power to alleviate a single affliction.

∞

It has ever been customary to leave coin and other offerings at a well in gratitude for illnesses prevented, cures received or afflictions mitigated. It is ill luck to steal even the smallest of these offerings and it is said that the pox first arose as a punishment of tinkers by wells whose stores of coin had been pilfered by those light-fingered travellers.

∞

To ensure that a well – whether it be enchanted or ordinary – continues to flow with good water, a procession must be made once a year around the well, the which, in the Gaelic is called a *deasil*. The people must come to the well and, bare-headed, they must each drink a single mouthful of its water, afterwards walking three times around the well, progressing, as goes the sun, from east to west. Blessings and incantations must be said, but these vary much among the islands and what is right in one place may be frowned upon in others. By general agreement, on leaving, each person must place a small offering of some sort upon the stone that covers the well.

∞

There is no safer place to hide a thing of value than within a well. This results from a peculiarity in the nature of wells that makes their content opaque to enchantment. Even spells of surpassing power, or seeing stones of the utmost clarity, cannot penetrate the depth of a well.

∞

The Five Pennies Well on the island of Eigg is efficacious against all ailments and those who dwell near it have remarkable robustness and health. Its virtues, however, are only bestowed upon those born on Eigg. Should a stranger drink its waters, the well has no beneficial effect. Visitors to the island are counselled not to sleep in the vicinity of the well for, should they do so, they will wake with a deformity. To sleep by the well for three nights means death, as befell a pedlar from Dundee who was found dead at the well with his body so covered with warts that his face could not be recognised.

∞

There was a well on the island of Colonsay whose water brought relief for womens' ailments. It was a powerful well and never failed countless generations of islanders. One day a woman from another island, newly married to a man of Colonsay, went to the well and disrespectfully washed her hands in it. Upon the instant the well dried, for to befoul a well of enchantment is an affront that will have a dire consequence. At the moment that the well ceased in Colonsay, it appeared anew in Islay, where it conferred its benefits upon the grateful people who treated it with all deference and respect, holding processions in its honour. It is known there as *Tobar na Cnabar*, meaning the well that walks from place to place.

∞

St Andrew's Well is amongst the most celebrated wells on the island of Lewis, despite that it has neither the power to cure ills, nor to prevent sickness. When a person lies betwixt life and death, however, it is said, the well waters unfailingly predict the possibility of recovery. A tub of well-water is placed at the bedside of the afflicted. Into this tub, a saucer or a plate is gently floated. Should the saucer sink, or should it move against the sun from west to east, then death is certain; but should the saucer move towards the west, in the sun's direction, then recovery is assured.

∞

The Isle of Jura has a well whose water is lighter by half than other waters. It is the sole well in all the world known to possess this quality and its water has many beneficial uses. The old, the young and the infirm can carry home full buckets from the well as the heaviness of the water, being halved, lies within their strength. Those leaving for a day's labour in the crofts, or along the shore, can drink twice the quantity of water without discomfort and, in this way, can work a full day and feel no thirst the while. A flask of this water, taken on a sea voyage, is curative of seasickness.

∞

There is a well at *Teampull Mor*, meaning 'the great temple', situated in proximity to the Butt of Lewis where once stood the Temple of St Molochus, now no more than a sorry ruin. Of all the wells on Lewis this one, called St Ronan's Well, brings the greatest relief from madness. To obtain this relief, the guardians of an afflicted person must first circle the sufferer seven times around the remains of the saint's temple. This being accomplished, the keeper of the well brings from it water in a diminutive jar, claimed by some to be a holy relic of the saint himself. So precious is this jar and the water therein that its custody is hereditary, the office of 'Clerk of the Temple' having passed from father to son for untold generations. An afflicted person, once having received a sprinkling of water from the jar, must be laid down and bound with ropes for the night on the altar stone within the ruins of the temple. If the sufferer falls into a sound sleep, the madness will depart and never return.

The Selkie from Lochlin

A FRAYING OCCURRED IN THE FIBRES that make up the knot of time at the exact moment the Princess Halldóra of Lochlin – in a last gesture of defiance – prepared to fling herself from the high cliff above Breakan's Cave. Along one thread of time Halldóra died, leaving behind the Seeing Stone in Lochlin to be found, generations later, by her descendant Princess Gradhag. It is through her that the Stone came to the pool at Baile na Cille, and the many accounts of Gradhag's drowning there attest to the truth and strength of this strand of the tale. There is however, another version; told less frequently but of equal weight, in which the Stone began its journey with Halldóra herself.

This telling, like many other renditions of the tale, describes how Princess Halldóra, grief-stricken from the drowning of her lover Breakan, rushed to the cliffs above Breakan's Cave. In the more popular versions of the tale she flung herself to her death on the rocks below. In this version, as she was about to scale the cliff to fulfill her dreadful intention, the Princess found herself observed by seven seals, awaiting her on the rocks. The largest of these rose up and removed its skin. Out stepped a man, who stood naked and beautiful, revealing himself to be a selkie. He called out "Princess Halldóra! Come to us, come to us, for we are your royal kin." Halldóra was arrested by his words and diverted from her terrible purpose. She descended towards him on the rocky shore until they stood level. He addressed Halldóra thus: "We seven, like you, are children of the royal blood of Lochlin. We became selkies through a malicious enchantment and must forever roam the seas. Join us and be honoured among our people." The selkie passed to her a second seal skin he carried and, too distraught to weigh the consequences, the Princess stepped into the perfect fit of it. The skin closed on her, wrapping her in its supple softness. Upon the instant, she was transformed into a grey seal. For several days she swam with the others in the clear cold of the water; she turned, she twisted, she revelled in the freely flowing sea upon her new skin. But after a month and a day her native land called to her and she longed, for one last time, to feel the solidity of Lochlin beneath her. She slid herself ashore and, as she basked among the rocks at Breakan's Cave with the other selkies, she realised that the figure of a man she could see standing on the cliff above was her father. With deliberate movements he was casting objects, which she suddenly understood to be her ornaments, down into the sea. In pity and grief Halldóra called to the King, but he did not understand her. She saw him toss the last object, which soared high, twisting in the air like a gull in flight, as if possessed of wings, glinting as it descended towards her. Halldóra knew what it must be even as it fell. In a trice the thing landed on her head and looped down around her neck, although she struggled in vain to shake it off. Sharp pain caught at her skin as she dipped her head and saw that it was the leather necklace set with silver fishhook barbs that ever tightened around her neck and embedded themselves in her so deeply that she could not escape. Against her throat the Princess felt the weight of the pebble she knew to be the Seeing Stone. Sorrow filled her. In despair Halldóra looked to the King on the cliff and for a moment held his gaze. Then she uttered a long, sad cry as a child might when torn from its parents and plunged under the waves, grieving for Breakan her prince and for the cruel twists of fortune that had befallen her.

Over the following days Halldóra listened to the other selkies describe to her the thing that was bound to her neck. She scraped it against rocks; she did all she could to catch it under sharp shells and to tug it loose, but in vain. The seer had woven his leather plait well and the Stone, which had been Halldóra's undoing, could not be budged from its embedded place on her neck. On the Eve of St John, just after midsummer, the selkies came ashore and she with them. There they took off their skins to dance upon the sand. She found that she too could remove her skin by wriggling free of the constriction around her neck, and this she did. Now she once more had human hands and thus great hopes that she might tug the necklace loose from the pelt lying on the sand before her. The Princess pulled with all her might but, although the seal skin was separate from her person, a sharp pain rose in her human neck as she tugged on the skin. The pain was so great she was forced to desist from her efforts.

Time passed and Halldóra came to gain an acceptance of her condition; her seal skin grew around and over the Stone and its necklace, so that naught could be seen of it. To the eye she seemed as any other grey seal, except that she had a ridge of pelt forming a collar around her neck, making her appear similar in shape to the seal rock at the entrance to the inlet on the Isle of Skye where, long ago, a royal Irish treasure fleet sheltered. Selkies travel widely and Halldóra came to know every coast from Norway to Erin. Her nature now revelled in the freedom of the sea and she remembered her former life as a prison of land, where movement was slow and effortful. She still emerged from the water with the other selkies three times each year to dance in the moonlight on the silver sand of deserted beaches. It was hard for her to shed her skin, however, because the pelt collar constricted her and it required much struggling to pull off or to put on. The dancing brought her bittersweet memories of toes digging into the sand, of the wind upon her human skin and the tossing of her heavy hair but none of these could compare with the wild freedom to dive effortlessly and wantonly beneath the waves.

It was while she swam among the deserted outer islands of North Uist that Halldóra became entangled once again with fate. Upon one of these islands Neil MacCodrum, with three companions from North Uist, was engaged in hunting for cormorants. As was the custom, one man was chosen to stand guard over the boat while the others clambered the cliffs with nets to ensnare the birds. That night, MacCodrum was guarding the boat as it sat in a narrow cove. The other men travelled across the spine of the island to the far cliffs and there they found cormorants aplenty. This was well for them because they had many uses for their prey.[12] The three men caught as many birds as they could carry, tying them around their waists so that they could lug more back with them.

Neil MacCodrum awaited their return. It was past midnight and the moon was full. He climbed the side of the cove to look at the beach beyond, and there he saw the strangest sight. A group of men and women were dancing on the sand. In the moonlight he could discern that they were most beautifully formed and more comely than any people he had ever before seen. And they danced naked. He called out to them. At the sound of his voice the men and women, Halldóra being among their number, started with great surprise. He clambered down the rocks to join them but they fled towards a pile of dark garments lying at the edge of the sea. As they pulled these garments upon themselves they transformed, one by one, into seals, and realisation came to Neil MacCodrum that these were selkies. Halldóra took much longer than the others as she had the greatest difficulty wriggling into the neck of her pelt. MacCodrum, in consequence, was able to catch her before she could dress. He pulled the sealskin from her.

"Give me my clothes!" Halldóra begged.

"That I shall not," said MacCodrum, "for I am desirous to know more of you and of whence you came."

"I was a Princess of Lochlin," Halldóra told him, "and now the sea is my true home. Let me return to it; give me back my pelt."

Neil MacCodrum looked intently at the beautiful woman who stood pleading before him and his heart was overcome with desire. "That I will not do," he replied, "for I shall take you with me and you shall be mine henceforth. Your skin I shall hide in a safe place."

He folded the skin and held it from her but handed her his coat to cover herself.

"I give you warning," cried Halldóra, "I cannot now be content upon the land. If ever I should find my skin I shall be away in the blinking of an eye."

The three hunters returned and they marvelled that MacCodrum had with him a woman of such surpassing beauty. They exchanged many curious and knowing glances, but they said nothing. All returned in the boat to North Uist with Neil MacCodrum sitting upon the seal skin so that it could not be taken from him. After the men had divided the cormorants among themselves, Neil returned with Halldóra to his croft. There she again made pleas that he should give back her pelt to her.

"I shall not," he said firmly, "I will hide it well where you can never discover it. You had best learn speedily that you are mine from this time forward."

Halldóra, seeing that there was no hope of changing Neil MacCodrum's intention, reconciled herself to her fate. "At the least you must promise to take good care of my skin," said she, "for if it cracks and breaks I shall die and I shall then be of little use to you."

"Of that you may be well assured," replied Neil, "I shall tend the pelt well, though it be hidden."

Selkies make the best wives for they have every virtue that a royal lineage can confer. They bear fine children, they are hard working and loyal; they are attentive to their husbands' every need. And so it was with Halldóra. She brought forth many children, mostly sons, who were healthy and happy. Neil MacCodrum blessed the day that he found her and counted himself the most fortunate of men. With each passing year, his love for her grew greater. He wanted her ever in his sight and his eyes followed her wherever she went. He was besotted with her and, because of this, he took good care to move the seal skin from time to time so that she might not discover it. Halldóra, for her part, searched for her pelt at every opportunity. But Neil was cunning and the skin's hiding places remained secret.

It is well said that although things may be hidden from men, nothing can be hidden long from children. Every day Halldóra enquired of the children whether, in their playing, they had chanced upon anything unexpected or extraordinary. She learned nothing from them until one day Neil moved the skin to a new hiding place. Then her eldest son told her, "I saw father put the most fine seal skin into a stack of corn and then cover it."

Upon the hearing of this, Halldóra was overjoyed. While Neil was away at the fishing, she ran to the corn stack and there she found her pelt. She called together her children. With tears in her eyes, and with the utmost tenderness, she told them that she must leave them. They walked down with her to the sea. There she took off her human clothes and folded them neatly, telling her eldest daughter to return them to her father. Halldóra pointed to a flat ledge at the side of the cove and said, "My children, I shall ever provide for you. Each morning, on that ledge, you shall find fish aplenty and this I shall do until the last of you is wed." So saying, and weeping as she did, she kissed each one. Then she struggled into her seal skin and was away, leaving her children grieving upon the shore.

When Neil MacCodrum returned he knew in an instant what had occurred. He was distraught and inconsolable. Next morning the children ran to the ledge and there they found fish laid out for them. Each following day there were freshly caught fish there, and this was well, for the bairns must needs take care of themselves as their father was too deep in his grief to apprehend the world around him. Sometimes, when they went to collect the fish, Halldóra's children saw a grey seal watching them from the sea and they knew well who it was, for around its neck there was a thickening that formed a collar.

Weeks later, as he recovered his senses, Neil MacCodrum rowed out in his boat. A grey seal came alongside and Neil pleaded with it and spoke lovingly. The seal wept but she could not leave her sea. This sad meeting was repeated many times, for no man who has had a selkie bride can forget her, even for a moment. It was through this same Neil MacCodrum that the Clan MacCodrum came to be. To this day, should a MacCodrum sit upon a rock, howsoever dry a day it might be, there will be dampness left behind and this dampness will resolve itself into crystals of salt. Neil MacCodrum, although the progenitor of this strong clan, was forever broken by the loss of his wife to the sea. Halldóra kept her promise and, until the last of her children was wed, she faithfully brought fish each day to the rock ledge. On the wedding day of her youngest daughter, she was away, never to return to North Uist and never to see Neil MacCodrum more.

Where it was that the selkie Halldóra journeyed next is a matter of conjecture. Some say that she went to the pool at Baile na Cille, for it is there that time loops back upon itself and the future becomes woven with the past. Others believe that she sojourned beneath the Minch among the Blue Men. It is without dispute that an event of the most extraordinary nature occurred after her departure from North Uist, so that the flow of time was in some manner metamorphosed. Whatever the difference in the accounts of her travels, there is general agreement that Halldóra reached the coast of Norway in an earlier age, and it was there that the strange circumstances of her death fulfilled ancient and powerful prophecies. It is on account of these circumstances that some scholars say that the history of the Seeing Stone of Lochlin commences there.

It was autumn in Norway, and the great Jarl and Earl of the Orkney Islands, Skule Tostesson, ordered a seal hunt to gather blubber and meat for the coming winter. The Jarl himself led the hunters and it was he who saw an old grey seal with distinctive markings around her neck very like a collar. The Jarl loosed an arrow which penetrated to the core and the grey seal fell, dying. At the instant the arrow hit its mark, the sky was filled with a curious light, as if the Nimble Men of the north sky were engaged in their wild dances.[13] For a moment, the whole firmament flickered and shimmered with colours far richer than a rainbow. The hunters stopped in wonderment, for none of them had seen such a thing before. Then the hunt resumed.

Tostesson thought no more of his kill and moved on to find new prey, leaving his vassals to skin the seal and to recover his arrowhead. He was preparing another arrow when he was interrupted by a commotion of shouts behind him. He turned and saw one of the skinners standing over the corpse of the old grey seal, holding up some object whose nature he could not discern. The Jarl returned to the spot and the man handed him the object, giving in explanation that he had cut it this very minute from the neck of the collared seal. Jarl Skule Tostesson examined it with the impatient curiosity for which he was known. In his hand was a leather plait, set with tarnished silver fishhook barbs, and hanging from it was a pale stone. He wiped blood from the leather and could discern runes burnt into the strips from which the neckpiece was made. The Jarl was about to cast it aside when he saw something that took all impatience from him and rooted him to the spot.

Burned into the leather he saw the runes of his own name, Skule Tostesson. He knew, in that moment, that this was an event of the most profound importance.

Jarl Skule Tostesson lost all appetite for hunting and returned to his hall to consult with seers, carrying with him the Stone on its plait. The seers examined it, exclaiming at the potent nature of the runes on the leather and noting that the Stone itself had faint rune-like markings. They conferred for a long time on the portent of the Jarl's name burned into the leather strip that had come from within the body of a seal. They told him that a prophecy, made by his grandfather's necromancer, had foretold that the name of Tostesson would rise from the sea, bringing a Stone that would guide his lineage. Jarl Skule Tostesson took the Stone from its plait of leather and held it in his hand. It fitted as if made for him alone. He sensed that he was holding a thing of great power. To commemorate the significance of what had occurred, he commissioned the making of a ring, set with a ruby in the shape of a seal. He further ordered a box of yew to be constructed, bound in silver and with a silver key. Into this box, with much ceremony, the Jarl and his seers placed the Stone.[14]

It is in this moment, some believe, that the history of the Seeing Stone of Lochlin truly begins.

On the Nature of Selkies

Folk of wisdom have said that to look into the eyes of a grey seal is to see all the sadness of the world. Royal blood runs in the veins of these seals and proof of this lies in the proud aspect of their gaze. Both the sadness of grey seals and their royal lineage are in consequence of an ancient and unfortunate happening.

The Queen of Lochlin was of Norse blood. She had, by the King, seven children, and they were handsome and fair. The Queen's happiness aroused the envy of a witch who, although of great beauty herself, had a venal heart given to spite. By use of poison and secret incantation, the witch caused the Queen of Lochlin to fall gravely ill. Despite all the efforts of the King and those about him, the Queen died. The King and his children were heartbroken.

The witch, seizing her opportunity for advancement, transformed herself into a likeness of the dead Queen and, in so doing, caused the King to fall in love with her. They married, and the King, perceiving within the woman reflections of and similarities to his lost beloved, was again happy. It was not so for the children, who sensed the witch's evil and sought to bring her faults to the attention of all. The witch therefore cast a spell upon the children, by this black deed transforming them forever into creatures of the sea, and it was in this way that they became the grey seals, the selkies.

It is in the nature of perpetual spells, however, that some mitigation or opportunity for temporary escape is required. In fulfillment of this, the witch wove into the fabric of the spell that her victims might on three nights in a year at the full moon, shed their sealskins and, for the duration of the night, resume their natural forms and roam again upon the land from whence they came.

∞

There is much argument as to whether all grey seals owe their creation to the Lochlin witchery, for if this should be true, every grey seal is endowed with the capacity to gain human form.

Some argue against this, believing that only the direct descendants of the seven children of Lochlin are able to take human form and that these are the true selkies, whilst the rest are but common seals. In support of this, they instance the infrequency with which selkies are seen. Conversely, those who contend that grey seals and selkies are one and the same say that the rarity of selkies upon the land is the result of many of them, having become contented with their life in the sea, no longer choosing to visit the land.

Others believe that some selkies remain at sea because they cannot bear the sadness of returning to human form and feeling again the land beneath their feet and the night wind through their hair.

∞

When selkies come ashore, they step out of their seal skins for, beneath these they possess perfect human form. Selkies cannot return to the sea except within their seal skins. By taking a selkie's pelt and hiding it, the unfortunate creature is compelled to remain upon the land.

There are many tales of men who have hidden skins in order to capture a selkie woman, known as they are to make the finest among brides. They are said to be beautiful, loyal and hard-working and they bear fine children. But they pine for their sea, which calls to them in a voice that grows ever stronger. A selkie woman who hears the call of the sea will hunt without rest for her hidden skin and, should she discover it, will don it and return immediately to her marine home. She will be forever saddened, for a selkie wife loves her husband and her children dearly, but the sea is in her blood and it will brook no denial.

∞

There is dispute as to the number of occasions that a selkie may come upon the land; some saying that it is but one night a year and that night being midsummer eve. Others aver that it is three or even four times, but only at the full moon. It is no great matter, for there is no exactness here, and there may be, among the clans of the selkies, different observances and customs. All agree, however, that the selkie-folk may not come freely upon the shore, unlike the fin-folk, from whom the mermen spring, who may come upon the land without restriction.

∞

A selkie skin is best hidden in a well, for many wells are opaque to seeing and a thing secreted in the depths of a well cannot be sensed by second sight. A well further ensures that the skin shall remain moist. Should a selkie skin become desiccated and cracked, the consequences are severe and beyond repair. If the hidden skin becomes dry, so does the human skin of its owner; if it cracks, then dreadful sores and cankers will result. As the skin dries, the very soul of the selkie withers; as the suppleness of the skin is lost, so does its human possessor lose spirit and life. If a selkie senses that her concealed skin has shrivelled beyond wearing, it is as if her very being were ended. She can no longer eat and will, unless restrained, walk into the sea to drown.

∞

Selkie men, in human form, are magically seductive and have great power over mortal women. It has been long known, among island peoples, that selkie men find unsatisfied shore-women and with them make havoc and mischief. Should a mortal woman desire a selkie lover, she must go to the shore at high tide and there shed seven tears into the sea. A handsome selkie will seek her out. It is said that a woman who has known a selkie consort can never again be satisfied by mortal man.

∞

Selkies have a love of singing and, if a woman with a fair voice sits upon the rocks and sings the old songs, or songs of loss, the sound will draw selkies from beneath the waves, the better to hear her, and they will weep profuse tears and sigh with a sadness that rends the heart. They care for songs in any tongue, but it is only for songs in the Gaelic that they weep.

∞

Many islanders have selkie blood in their veins. The test for this is the mark of dampness visible upon an otherwise dry rock where they have been seated for a time. As the dampness dries, small salt crystals form. Many consider this to be an infallible guide to determine selkie lineage.

∞

The finest harpist of South Uist was Calum Macphail, a bard and storyteller beyond compare. His voice was so sweet that whenever he sang even the animals came to hear him. His mother was a selkie and, though she never told him that she was of the sea, she taught him the selkie legends and songs and these informed his singing. When he was a young man he found a sealskin hidden in a pook of hay and, ignorant of its meaning, took it home to show his mother. She was overjoyed by this, as she had reached the time when the sea was calling her back. She took the skin and, in a trice, was into it and away. Ever after, the bard would walk by the sea and would talk to the seals. But were not his songs the sweetest and the saddest ever to be heard in all the islands?

∞

The Lady Ursilla of Orkney married on a whim to a man beneath her station and, in so doing, was shunned by her friends of high birth. She became lonely and her husband, who was indeed a clod, was of little comfort to her. Knowing a means to remedy her situation, she wept seven tears into the sea and summoned forth a selkie lover, keeping her amorous liaison a secret from her husband.

Ursilla bore seven children and each one had webs between the fingers and webs between the toes very like a selkie's paws. Although at birth the midwife snipped away these webs, they slowly regrew and

Ursilla kept a pair of silver shears to clip away the proof of her infidelities. But indiscretion of this magnitude cannot be so readily hidden.

As the children grew, a horny membrane formed over their hands and feet. To this day, certain of her descendants have that incriminating crust upon their hands and it has made for them a sorry plight, for they cannot well row a boat or farm the land.

The Stone at Brahan

THE PROPHECIES OF KENNETH ODHAR, the Seer of Brahan, are well known throughout Scotland. It is taught in schools that Odhar was born on the Isle of Lewis near Baile na Cille, that he worked on the Seaforth estate at Brahan and that he became a powerful visionary whose prophecies rivalled those of Nostrodamus. Many of his predictions have already manifestly come to pass. Through the natural progression of time, yet other of his unfulfilled prognostications may also come to fruition. There will remain, however, of his numerous prophecies, some small few that will stay forever unachieved and the cause of this is that seeing stones may search along more than one thread in the fabric of time for their *seeings*. A prediction, that would seem unfulfilled in the world we know, may already have proved itself true along a different strand of time. The genius of Kenneth Odhar was that his eye was skilled in discernment. He could pick out the correct thread of our future from many enticing alternative possibilities and thus many of his prophecies have verifiably come to pass within our time. In this way he predicted with greater accuracy than other seers, who have sometimes been misled through seeing future events along a path of time that is not ours.

142

The clarity of Kenneth Odhar's vision was the more remarkable for a man whose life was so closely linked to the pool at Baile na Cille, where the very nature of time twists upon itself and becomes opaque. It is not the purpose here to delineate or comment upon the Seer's fulfilled prophecies, for they are a matter of record and there is little reason to repeat what is already so well established. The intent of this telling, instead, is to follow the Seeing Stone and to chronicle the ways in which it affected the course of events and the lives of those who held it. And nowhere were these changes more evident or more profound than at Brahan.

The return of Kenneth Mor MacKenzie from his incarceration at Inverness castle had lifted the cloud of gloom and fear that loomed over the Brahan estate during his absence. He was in unaccustomed good humour and bestowed favours liberally. His new bride, Isabella of Tarbat, sparkled with the radiance of a newly-wed. She was admired by all and, when she went riding, men and women ceased their work to watch her pass. Her flowing red hair became the subject of much discussion. Some said that she maintained its lustre through the daily eating of beetroot; others ascribed the vibrancy of her tresses to a tincture made from rare oranges. A few muttered darkly that her hair was the colour of blood because it was with blood that she washed it. Her presence at Brahan brought a lightness of heart to all who depended for their livelihood upon the Laird's estate. She arranged dances in the great stone barn and its walls rang with the strains of the pipes and with merriment. Alone among the estate workers, only Kenneth Odhar was resistant to the general cheer. He became reclusive and was no longer to be seen at estate gatherings unless his presence had been commanded by the Earl or his factor. Kenneth, instead, spent much time alone, brooding upon his fate. He often took the Stone from its leathern pouch and, turning it over and over in his palm, was strangely comforted by how perfectly it fitted his hand. He was loath to put it to his eye and tussled mightily within himself on the dangers the Stone might hold for him.

After much inner debate, he reasoned that it was not the Stone itself that threatened him. Instead it was the future misadventure with a red-haired woman, as foretold by his mother, that he should fear. The Stone was not the cause of the dire prophecy; it was no more than the vessel through which the prophecy had become apparent. Kenneth knew that, whatever the consequences, soon he would raise the Stone to look through its perfect aperture.

One morning he woke fired with a defiant resolve. He took out the Stone and put it to his good right eye. At first he discerned nothing beyond the ordinary. Although the scene before him was unchanged, viewed through the Stone there was an added crispness to the landscape as if it had become illumined by the sharpness of a flinty winter sun. He lowered it, then raised the Stone again and observed the same effect. He waited. Then Kenneth Odhar put the Stone to his weak left eye and was overcome with wonder at the clarity with which he saw the scene before him. Detail that was heretofore inaccessible, even to his good eye, was now so exact and particular that he could even discriminate the individual filaments of a moss growing on a distant rock.

Now Kenneth Odhar was a cautious man. Although he felt elation from his first seeing, and although he trembled with the excitement of it, he nevertheless elected not to use the Stone again that morning. He replaced it in its pouch of ewe leather and went about his business. The next day was the Sabbath, in consequence of which he dressed in his best and walked to the church at Kintail. There the Reverend Farquhar MacRae, who had the living of the parish and was Kenneth's former teacher, preached a sermon upon a text from the book of Samuel, "*For rebellion was as the sin of witchcraft*". In his sermon, MacRae waxed eloquent upon the twin evils of insurrection and superstition. He enjoined his congregation to accept their lot humbly and with a good grace. He poured scorn on those who believed in the old ways and lamented that, in this enlightened age of science and discovery, the ignorant Scot was forever kept low, being disadvantaged by antiquated and mistaken beliefs.

As he walked home, Kenneth Odhar pondered upon what he had heard. What if the otherworld was, as MacRae preached, a mere superstition? If the prophecies of his death at the hands of a red-headed woman were ignorant or mistaken? His mother had taught him respect for the old ways, but what if she had become deranged? Could he spend his life fearing a curse that might exist only within the imagination of a superstitious woman? As he walked his heart lightened and he made a decision that would change his life. Arriving at his cottage he made his way directly to the leathern pouch and from it withdrew the Stone. He put it to his weak left eye and was immediately rewarded with scenes of unmatched clarity. Yet he saw no prophecy; the world he viewed through the Stone was no more than the world of the present seen through a spyglass. Then, out of the corner of his eye, within the Stone, he glimpsed Isabella of Tarbat riding her white horse. Kenneth looked directly at the image and it disappeared. When he looked away, there it was again. Cautiously he moved the focus of his gaze towards the vision and found that it remained, providing he looked discreetly – much as a man might steal a glimpse of an elegant lady in church while feigning full attention to the sermon. He could observe clearly enough that Isabella was crossing a small burn. He saw her horse slip as it climbed the bank, toppling the rider into the mud. Isabella rose unhurt, her fine clothes dirtied, and she remounted. The vision faded and the Stone elected to show him no more. Kenneth reasoned that what he had seen must lie in the past or in the future, for today was the Sabbath and the Lady Isabella would not, at this moment, be indulging in untoward worldly enjoyments such as riding for pleasure.

Next day was washing day at Brahan and he was summoned to the estate laundry to clear a blocked drain. A laundry maid came running, carrying in her arms soiled riding clothes. She told all who would give ear that her lady had had a mishap with her horse at the south burn this very morning and had returned with her beautiful clothes soiled beyond all power of washing to redress. Kenneth mulled over what he heard. The Stone had given him sight of an accident a full twelve hours before its occurrence. Might this, he wondered, be a result of the witchcraft and superstition that the Reverend Farquhar MacRae had so fiercely decried? Or was it no more than an everyday coincidence, of which folks made much although it meant but little? His return path took him by the factor's house and there he saw the factor's son in the garden, gazing through a tube with glass lenses. Kenneth knew this to be a telescope, for he had seen seafaring men using them before, although he had never himself looked through a telescope lens. He asked the lad for a viewing and saw, with some amazement, that the telescope did, indeed, bring a degree of closeness to distant objects, although the clarity of the instrument faded compared with the sharpness of vision afforded by his Stone. The factor himself emerged from the house and remarked to Kenneth that the telescope was a boon to mankind and a perfect example of the age of science and discovery which had been extolled by MacRae in yesterday's sermon. Kenneth was much reassured by this. The Seeing Stone, he told himself, was but a telescope that saw the future. It was an instrument of discovery, and there was no culpable superstition or witchcraft in its use. The factor had unwittingly conferred legitimacy on his use of the Stone.

In the weeks that followed, Kenneth Odhar worked diligently to master the ways of his Stone. He found that it was subtle and required a gentle touch. Not only must he look through it indirectly, he must also *think* indirectly when using it. His fascination with Isabella led him to employ the Stone to see further happenings relating to her. He soon found, however, that when he concentrated his mind upon her person, he discerned nothing. Instead he learned first to empty himself of all thought and to suppress the tantalising visions of her flowing red hair that so readily filled his imagination. Then, cautiously, if he allowed nothing but the quietest perception of her to enter into his consciousness, he could see her there within the Stone's aperture. In this way Kenneth learned to call up apparitions of Isabella at will, although everything he saw remained mundane and unremarkable. In the same fashion, he saw the doings of Kenneth Mor MacKenzie and was thrown into confusion and awkwardness by certain sights that the Stone revealed. The Laird was engaged in a dalliance with a lady of remarkable beauty from Kintail, whose husband was away in England. The Stone seemed to take a perverse delight in showing Odhar every detail of their lascivious activities. Kenneth was shy in the presence of women and was so disconcerted by the Stone's lewdness that he resolved not to observe any further doings of the Laird.

As he became familiar with the ways of the Stone, Odhar realised that it often showed him more than one version of an event, leaving him to decide which account was the better representation of truth. Sometimes these versions varied only in their minutest particulars. In one instance he saw Isabella and two of her maids in the castle's kitchen garden. A cat had caught a sparrow and the ladies chased after it. He put the Stone again to his eye and this time watched an identical scene, except that the cat's victim was now a robin. Kenneth became adept at seeking clues from these sightings to determine which of the Stone's accounts were to be relied upon. One day he saw a magpie steal a pearl ring from Isabella's chamber and fly off with it to decorate its untidy nest in a hawthorn tree behind the estate stables. When he repeated the sighting it was a jackdaw which thieved the ring and took it to the ruins of an ancient castle keep where she had made her home. Kenneth Odhar had a keen memory for detail. In the sighting with the magpie his attention rested for a moment on a patch of thistles

147

between the hawthorn tree and the stable wall that he could not recall having seen before. To ascertain the accuracy of this, he went to the stable and found that his recollection was correct; there were no thistles there. In consequence, he decided that the jackdaw, and not the magpie, was the thief.

While he was walking behind the stables he came across Lady Isabella's chambermaid much distressed, being under a cloud of suspicion because her lady was missing a valuable ring. Kenneth told the maid that he had knowledge that a pearl ring had been stolen from Isabella's chamber by a jackdaw and that the same ring could be found secreted in a nest within the ruined keep. The maid conveyed this information to her mistress and soon the missing ring was recovered. Lady Isabella of Tarbat was intrigued that a worker on her husband's estate should have such ready knowledge of the ring's whereabouts and summoned Kenneth. He readily acknowledged that he had seen the theft of the ring using a seeing stone. Isabella privately doubted his account, supposing that he and her maid were likely conspirators who had hidden the ring within the nest, hoping to secrete it away when the commotion caused by its disappearance had subsided. She resolved to put Kenneth to a test to determine his veracity and asked him to use the Stone to see the condition of her father, Lord Tarbat. In doing this, she set a trap for Kenneth. She privately knew that her father was in danger of disgrace and was under suspicion of being party to insurrection. Kenneth had difficulty in his seeing. He had not used the Stone to see distant events before and he had no personal knowledge of Tarbat to help him summon up an image. He faltered and, in doing so, intensified Isabella's suspicions. He made several attempts to see the disposition of Lord Tarbat but failed to provoke an image from the Stone.

Isabella accused him of fabricating his seeing ability as a ruse to disguise his part in the theft of her ring, which she averred was her dearest possession as it had been given to her by her father himself. Kenneth asked to touch the ring to give him a tangible connection with Lord Tarbat that might aid his seeing. With some reluctance and considerable suspicion, Isabella allowed this. Kenneth put the Stone to his weak eye and immediately saw Lord Tarbat receiving good news. He told Isabella, "Your father is a happy man, for he has received the King's pardon and is appointed this day Lord Justice General of Scotland." Isabella was disbelieving, knowing this news to be improbable in the extreme. The office of Justice General had been held for many generations in the Argyle clan and was theirs by hereditary right. Nevertheless, Kenneth was able to describe details of Lord Tarbat's great hall and could give a good account of his manner of dress that bespoke a knowledge beyond that of a base imposter. The Lady Isabella could not entirely disbelieve Kenneth Odhar, yet his claim that her father was in the King's high favour seemed the kind of fanciful dross of fortune tellers and mountebanks. She sent him away, believing him to be Guilty not Proven, and resolved to keep a close watch on his activities.

Two days later word arrived from Lord Tarbat that his fortunes had been miraculously restored, to the astonishment of all. He had, indeed, received the King's commission appointing him Lord Justice General of Scotland, the office having been stripped from the Argyles. Isabella now apprehended that Kenneth Odhar had a rare power that she might in future use to her advantage. She summoned his attendance and gave him a reward of ten shillings for his part in the recovery of her ring and she was fulsome in her praise of him to her husband, the Earl.

On the Nature of Women with Red Hair

In the days before history, when the sum of mankind was small and scattered, the hair of every woman was of the same brown colour. At that time, there was a king of the northlands named Alef, who was the son of a god and, in consequence, born as an immortal. He fell in love with a lowborn Norse woman and married her against the wishes of his father. In retribution for this disobedience, the gods revoked Alef's immortality. In mitigation of this severe sentence, however, they agreed that his children, although destined to be mortal, should be given a special attribute that would make each one unique in the world.

Alef had three daughters. The eldest daughter was the first woman ever to be born with fair hair; to her the gods gave the gift of bringing sunlight wherever she went. The second daughter was the first woman to be born with black hair and the gods gifted her with the powers of night. The youngest daughter was born with red hair and to her the gods bestowed the gift of fire. Perhaps it is from this that the legends of hot-tempered red-haired women spring. Certainly it is from her that all red-headed people are descended and from her stock came the first smiths, who learned to smelt metals.

∞

Second sight is strongest in women with red hair, an instance being Margaret, the mother of the Brahan Seer, whose second sight was legendary. Many of these women, having given birth to daughters with hair as red as their own, have employed potions, spells and magic to suppress the gift in their daughters before it might develop into full second sight. These attempts, prompted by the belief that second sight is more of a curse than a blessing, have generally been unsuccessful. A tincture made from yew berries boiled in water from the walking well of Islay, *Tobar na Cnabar,* has been shown to be partially effective if placed in a raven's skull and administered with a silver spoon. It has been reliably observed that if a red-headed woman with second sight dyes her hair, her seeing will remain unaffected.

∞

Yew berries are lethal to all but red-headed women, who are said to be able to eat them with impunity. It has been widely rumoured that Fingal of Achintore, a bard of great repute, was poisoned by his red-headed wife, who employed for the purpose a lamb stew liberally laced with yew berries. The authorities, who knew nothing of her immunity to the effects of yew, were satisfied that his death was from some other cause, as she had eaten well of the same stew. But those with better knowledge of the old ways knew the truth.

∞

Kelpies, or water horses, are malevolent shape-shifting creatures that live beneath the water in the depths of certain lochs. They prey upon the unsuspecting and gullible and, in this respect, they find their victims most readily amongst children and young women of a romantic and dreamy nature. Kelpies ensnare children by enticing them to ride upon their backs, whereupon they gallop away, carrying them beneath the water. On encountering a young woman, a kelpie takes the form of a personable young man wearing a silver necklace. So great is the young man's charm that most impressionable young women cannot resist. Red-headed girls, however, if they should touch the silver necklace around the kelpie's neck, cause the pendant to turn instantly into a horse collar, whereat the kelpie will revert to its horse shape and gallop away.

∞

The most dangerous of all women are the *baobhan sith* who prey upon unsuspecting men, sucking their blood. These women are invariably beautiful and dress in white. Because of this manner of dress, they are sometimes known as 'The White Women of the Highlands'. Those few men who have encountered the *baobhan sith* and escaped with their lives, however, generally report that the hair of the seductress who accosted them was vibrantly red.

∞

The *dearg-due,* translated as 'red blood suckers', are women forced into unhappy marriages. In the unbearable extremity of their predicament, they kill themselves. Should the unfortunate woman have red hair, she will rise from her unconsecrated grave at the next full moon and gain her revenge by murdering both her father and her husband. It is thought that if such women fail in their attempted retribution, they wander forever and become *baobhan sith,* seeking revenge on any solitary men they encounter. There has been no satisfactory explanation offered as to why only red-headed women are affected in this manner.

∞

Red-headed women are not stronger than other women in the normal course of affairs. But if their temper is aroused, there is a fire within them that gives them the strength of several brawny men.

The wife of the smith of Timsgarry was visiting her neighbours in Ardroil when one told her that her husband was engaged in a clandestine dalliance with a woman from Valtos. The smith's wife flew into such a rage that some who saw it say her red hair glowed with the intensity of the fire in the smithy forge. Then and there she swore to kill her husband. Three strong men tried to restrain her but she dragged them with her all the way back to Timsgarry, threatening vengeance on her errant husband the while. Arriving at the forge, she picked up an anvil, which weighed as much as two grown men, and flung it at the smith. It missed him, but embedded itself deep in the wall of the smithy, where it remained for many years to remind him that his next dalliance would cost him his life.

Many reliable witnesses have seen the anvil lodged there, so we can be certain from their accounts that this is a true tale.

Of Carvers and Sagas

A FULL CENTURY BEFORE Isabella of Tarbat will set eyes on Kenneth Odhar at Brahan, a man will be arrested on the Isle of Skye for the practice of witchcraft. Even his name will be a matter of dispute. The Warrant of Detention will name him as Coinneach Odhar but he will also be called, variously, Kenneth Mor and Keanoch Owir. The several accounts of his trial may disagree as to his name, but in one respect they will be unanimous. The man will be charged with possession and use of a seeing stone for the purposes of witchcraft: a stone that will be described as *being possessed of unnatural and malignant capabilities*. For this reason, many believe the man to have been the Brahan Seer himself. His appearance, more than a hundred years before the famous events at Brahan, is a further instance of time twisting back upon itself, as it has done several times now in the unfolding story of the Seeing Stone.

It is a matter of considerable interest to Stone scholars as to whether the seeing stone described in the records on Skye is the Stone itself and, if so, the circumstances whereby the Stone might have reached Skye. Complicating the hunt for the provenance of this stone is the uncertainty of time itself. Does the appearance of the Stone in Skye, long before the events at Baile na Cille and

Brahan, suggest that time might at some point in the future, move back upon itself? And, if that is so, which threads of this tale are in the past and which in the future? If the events in Skye exist along our own thread of time, there must be an explanation as to how the Stone arrived there. None of the other narratives we have considered provide this.

An obscure account from Norse sources links the Stone of Skule Tostesson with the business on Skye. This account, like many others, cannot be placed with certainty in a particular time and has been described for that reason as *a story of a future that is past*. Because of its twists and recursions, the account is complex and, perhaps because of that, is rarely told.

The tale begins on Trondheim fjord in Norway, with preparations for a voyage by Tostig Godwinson, the great-great-grandson of Jarl Skule Tostesson. Unlike his illustrious ancestor, Godwinson was a poor trader, not a rich raider. He had but a single ship, heavy and slow. This one ship, and a near worthless collection of casting runes and seeing stones, were the only remnants of the vast Tostesson estates passed down to him by his father. His father's testament of inheritance described this motley collection with the words, *for my youngest son: a trading ship and a yew box containing certain instruments of divination that in former superstitious times were held by our forebears to foresee the future*. In a later age, scholars will quote this testament as a clear indication that the great Stone of Jarl Skule Tostesson was passed into the hands of his great-great-grandson.

As an impoverished but aspiring trader, Tostig Godwinson had many more issues on his mind than the Stone and its provenance. The yew box lay forgotten and undisturbed within his cabin while he contemplated more pressing difficulties. Although his ship was heavy, its cargo space was limited. Its stout nature would have been of greatest advantage to him in the northern oceans, where it would have proved the perfect vessel for the stormy crossings from Norway to Iceland and perhaps beyond to Greenland. But the limited capacity of his craft meant that he would be unable to make a good living carrying the usual bulky cargoes of grain and wood to Iceland. Godwinson occupied his thoughts with finding a more profitable cargo. His thinking was to yield little of substance until chance intervened.[15]

On the occasion of his elder brother's wedding, Tostig Godwinson met the Archbishop of Trondheim, who showed him a chess set carved from walrus ivory. The Archbishop told him that the best carving ivory came from Greenland but was then in such short supply that the carvers of Trondheim were willing to pay its weight in gold for a fine tusk. Tostig Godwinson instantly understood what his future cargoes would be. The following spring he set forth for Iceland with five companions. He hoped to buy ivory, for the Archbishop had told him that good Greenland ivory was readily available there. For outward cargo, the ship carried iron pots, these being in great demand for the Icelanders lacked the capability to smelt iron. He also carried letters from the Archbishop of Trondheim to the Bishop of Iceland. For safety, Godwinson placed these letters in the yew box that held his inherited seeing stones, and carefully sealed the edges of the box with wax to keep the seawater from damaging the contents.

On arrival in Skálholt, Iceland, Godwinson sold his cargo of iron pots and dutifully unsealed the yew box, extracting the letters and delivering them to Páll Jónsson, the Bishop of Iceland. He found the Bishop to be a simple man who lived modestly with his wife Margrét. It transpired that Margrét was an ivory carver of unsurpassed skill. She would live to be called Margrét the Adroit by Icelanders, and she would earn a future place in Icelandic history for the exquisite quality of the ivory from the little workshop that she would one day run with Thorsteinn the Schrinesmith. Tostig Godwinson saw some of her carvings and realised that they were unquestionably superior to the fine carvings of chessmen the Archbishop had so proudly shown him back in Trondheim. He told the Bishop and his wife of this and the Bishop made a proposition. "Suppose," he said, "that we produce a chess set for the Archbishop as a gift for the help he has provided us over these many years. And, as a tribute to him, instead of the elephant pieces, Margrét could, in their place, carve bishops."[16]

All were delighted by this elegant idea and it was agreed that Margrét would commence the carving. Because the intricacy of the work would require a month or more of delicate labour, it was agreed that, during the waiting time, Godwinson and his crew would go to Greenland, to hunt walrus and bring back new supplies of ivory. This they did, returning with a rich haul of walrus tusks. Godwinson, who had the trader's knack of seeking the greatest advantage from every transaction, had a proposition for Margrét when they returned. He commissioned her to carve a further five chess sets while he carried the Archbishop's gift back to Trondheim, together with the larger part of his tusk cargo. He arranged to return the following spring to collect the new chess sets and a cargo of additional tusks.

Godwinson's reception in Trondheim exceeded his most optimistic imaginings. The Archbishop was amazed and delighted at the gift. The ivory carvers of Trondheim jostled to gaze on these pieces and willingly paid the best prices for Godwinson's cargo of tusks. The fame of the carvings spread well beyond the ivory craftsmen. So celebrated did the chessmen become that woodworkers copied Margrét's intricate designs as they carved the new pews in Trondheim cathedral. The chess set became the talk of Trondheim. A visiting emissary from the High Irish court at Tara offered an unheard-of price if similar sets could be made for his masters. Godwinson revealed that five further sets were being created and agreed to deliver four of them to Ireland the following summer.

At first, the venture went well and Tostig Godwinson returned to Skálholt a happy man. Margrét and her craftsmen had completed four of the five new chess sets and all agreed that they were even finer than the pieces of the Archbishop's gift. Whilst waiting for the fifth and final set to be completed, which took a long summer month, the crew amused themselves with fishing and walrus hunting. Tostig Godwinson, however, was preoccupied by a different consideration. The Bishop had been making written copies of the great Icelandic Sagas. "These are treasures even beyond the carvings of Margrét," he said. "The greatest poetry of the ages and all in the heads of bards who could be gone in an eye-blink and take with them to their graves sublime verses such as the world shall never hear again." Godwinson read the Bishop's transcriptions and was enchanted. He was stirred by the heroic deeds they described and by the magnificent language of the Old Norse tongue. He went with Bishop Jónsson to hear an ancient bard recite *Egil's Saga* by the great Icelandic poet, Egill Skallagrímsson. The bard declaimed in the high skaldic manner, his voice thrilling and resonant. For his listeners, time stopped and the whole world was filled with the intricate and compelling Old High Tongue. When the bard finished, Godwinson sat transfixed, unable to move, poised between ecstasy and exhaustion. The next night he went to the recital again, and the next. He tried to learn the words, their stresses, their many allusions and alliterations but felt himself defeated by their complexity.

Tostig Godwinson decided to take writing materials with him to the final night's recital, hoping to capture at least part of a stanza. He returned to his ship and searched in his yew box for vellum. As he opened the box Godwinson was greatly startled to hear a strange bardic voice within his head, declaiming a single rhyming stanza from the *Hofuðlausn* saga. He slammed shut the lid and the voice became muffled and died. Cautiously, he reopened it and there it was in his head again. He did not know that it was the Stone within the box, calling out the verse to tempt him to pick it up, and so he believed that the yew box itself must be the source of this magic. He ignored the Stone and continued to open and close the box repeatedly in order to hear the poet's words.[17] He did not know that the voice he could hear was that of the great poet Egill Skallagrímsson himself, brought by the Stone as an echo, a sound vision from an earlier time.

After a hundred listenings the stanza was just as firmly implanted in Godwinson's memory as the childhood songs he had heard from his nurse. He even ventured to recite it to the Bishop and the bard, who could scarcely believe their ears. Both men exclaimed with amazement at the sea trader's unexpected mastery of the intricacy of high skaldic verse. Neither one of them suspected that enchantment was the cause, instead ascribing Godwinson's achievement to his natural and native talents and his unexpected enthusiasm for the poetry of *Egil's Saga*.

At length the final chess set was completed and Godwinson readied his ship for the crossing to Trondheim, where he planned to unload and sell his new cargo of ivory tusks. In preparation for the voyage, he placed letters to Trondheim from Bishop Jónsson in the yew box and sealed it again with wax, oblivious to the Stone and its entreaties. Finally, with great care, he wrapped each of the five chess sets in sealskin and stowed them in a place of safety until he was ready to leave. He bade farewell to Bishop Páll Jónsson and to Margrét, promising to return the following spring, a promise he would never be permitted to keep. After an uneventful voyage Godwinson arrived in Trondheim, retrieved the letters from the yew box and delivered them safely to the Archbishop. After some thought he decided that it would be in poor taste to show the Archbishop these new chessmen, as their quality quite eclipsed that of his gifted set. So he made no mention of the new carvings and, instead, busied himself with the sale of his cargo of tusks, at gratifyingly high prices.

From Trondheim Godwinson sailed for Ireland, carrying with him the precious carved ivory chess sets. The winds were fair and the sea calm. The ship made good progress south along the Scottish coast, mooring for the night at the entrance to a sea cave on the island of Tanera Mor, the largest of the Summer Isles and within two days' sailing of Skye. The intent of Godwinson and his crew was to replenish in Skye and then, after traversing the seas of the southern Minch, to set a course for the Boyle River in Ireland where the High King of Ireland held court at Tara. That night, the crew was awakened by shouting and clashing from the neighbouring Horse Island, a couple of leagues to the south-west and directly on their intended course. They could see flames and destruction clearly across the darkened sea and were at once filled with the apprehension that raiders were in their vicinity. They argued as to their best course of action.

"Turn back," urged a young crew member. "No! Stay here within the cave and hope to escape notice," counselled the steersman. Tostig Godwinson, ever a cautious man, decided on a safer course of action; he looked for a place to hide his precious cargo. His eyes lit upon a pot of porridge that the sailors had prepared for their meal and which now sat cooling and uneaten. Quickly he submerged one set of chessmen within the lukewarm pot, but realised there was no room there for the others.

Godwinson took the decision to hide the remaining chess sets on a dry ledge deep within the sea cave. "If we leave the other four sets of chessmen hidden here," he told his men, "our ship will seem to be empty and we will be allowed to pass. We shall replenish in one of the safe harbours of Skye and then return for the rest of the chessmen once the pirates have gone." He further reasoned that the ship itself would be spared as neither its slow and heavy nature nor its small carrying capacity would be of use to raiders.

Leaving the safe confines of the cave, Godwinson's vessel sailed on and into the path of the raiders. His predictions proved only partly correct. The pirates, it transpired, were not pirates at all, despite the fearsome appearance of their leader, Malcolm MacLeod, a huge red-headed man dressed in black with a patch over his left eye.[18] They were, instead, a revenge party of MacLeods intent on exacting retribution from the island community for a supposed wrong. The MacLeods searched the vessel to satisfy themselves that Godwinson's crew carried nothing of value. All they discovered was a pot of cold porridge, together with a yew trinket box containing a number of worthless pebbles and a set of small stones inscribed with runes they could not understand. The MacLeods willingly let the ship continue to Skye and even offered the crew good wishes for their crossing.

The MacLeod party, their revenge on Horse Island completed, sailed north, looking for a sheltered mooring for the night and chanced upon the same sea cave where the chess sets were hidden. It has been said of chance that although it may be too intricate to understand, it is never without its own purpose. As if it had been ordained, the MacLeod men quickly discovered the ledge holding many exquisite miniature figures carved from walrus ivory. The MacLeods were not educated men and they were saturated with many superstitions. The game of chess was unknown to them and they wondered considerably among themselves as to the purpose of this display of statuary. They saw that many of the figures appeared to be nobles and fighting men and, in consequence, they supposed that this cave must be the sacred burial place of kings and mighty warriors. Suddenly fearing the retribution of spirits, they left the chessmen untouched and, feeling uneasy in the presence of power and mystery, weighed anchor and sailed further north to an alternative anchorage in Old Dornie Bay. In this way they would fulfil the Brahan Seer's prophecy that a one-eyed MacLeod will discover a legendary treasure on Tanera Mor.[19]

Tostig Godwinson and his party waited for many hours, drifting on the sea, until they deemed it safe to reverse their course and return to Tanera Mor. There they retrieved the four hidden chess sets and headed from the cave into the Minch, setting course for

Skye. Not knowing of the Blue Men and their fearsome reputation, they thought little of the swirlings of blue, green and grey waters around the ship. They were unaware that a sea-knot was being prepared for their destruction. Three Blue Men rose up from the roiling seas and, as is their custom, challenged the ship's captain to a contest of rhyme and riddles. It was at this juncture that Godwinson made an uncharacteristically bold move.[20] He called out in his native Old Norse that he would respond to their challenge if he himself could recite the first rhyme and put the first riddle. The crew members looked towards each other, wild-eyed. They knew that their captain was no poet and they were chilled with fear at what might come of this contest. The Blue Men consulted with each other. It is their long-held custom to begin both rhyme and riddle themselves. In deference to Godwinson's boldness, however, and the way that he had addressed them in the old tongue, they finally consented.

Tostig Godwinson stood tall on the deck of his ship and, with the authority of a true bard, began to declaim his stanza from the *Egil's Saga*:

I, borne on song-tides
With strong set course,
Faced toward sun-tithe
From Odin's shores –
My oaken heart-hull
Bit through the frost's bite,
Of bright glories full –
And I sang them right.[21]

The Blue Men were silent as he completed the stanza. Godwinson had spoken in the high skaldic *runhent* metre. He had displayed the deepest level of rhyming skill. The Blue Men venerate this style and knew they were unable to match such poetic intricacy. They moved on to the riddle.

Godwinson commenced the riddle by holding high the pot of porridge so that it might readily be seen by the Blue Men. "In this porridge pot," he shouted, "are two armies in a constant war. Explain how this can be." Shifting uncomfortably on the vessel's prow, the Blue Men were bemused. The pot, they reasoned, was too small to hold a single dwarf. It could not possibly contain two armies. So they challenged the captain to prove the claim of his riddle or to be sent forthwith to the bottom of the Minch. "If I prove my claim, and if you will permit us to pass unhindered to Skye," he promised, "I shall deliver both armies into your possession and they will forever battle each other for your amusement and delight."

This offer proved irresistible to the Blue Men, who were amazed when the chessmen were uncovered and displayed to them. True to their word, once the chess set was in their possession, they allowed the boat, and the four remaining chess sets, to continue to Skye unimpeded.

In Skye, the crew reprovisioned their ship. They planned a course to take them through the north channel and down the east coast of Ireland to the mouth of the River Boyne. They were about to embark on this journey when a battered Irish ship entered the harbour, bearing news that the Boyne was blockaded by men of the Corcu Loígde and the Connachta, who were caught up in a feud with the High King of Ireland. Tostig Godwinson and his crew were thrown into a quandary. On the one hand they were tempted by the promised fortune to be paid by the Court for their cargo; on the other they feared that if the High King were to be defeated by the feuding tribes there would be no reward for them except theft of their cargo or even death.

It is at this point in the tale that Kenneth Odhar, or Keanoch Owir, first makes an appearance. Godwinson heard of a seer on Skye with unnatural powers of prophecy who could foretell distant events and predict the outcome of any course of action. After some enquiry and search, he discovered that this seer, Kenneth Odhar, lived at Carbost, on the south shore of Loch Harport, where he was associated with a group of men engaged in the illicit production of *uisge beatha*, the water of life. At first Odhar would not speak with him but, once assured that Godwinson was no excise man, agreed to a meeting. Odhar made a strange offer: in exchange for a stone of his choosing from a yew box in the possession of Tostig Godwinson, he would foretell the most propitious course for the ship to take. An agreement was reached and the Seer chose a pale pebble with a hole through it from the box. It fitted his hand as if made for it. Holding it to his eye, he told Godwinson that he could see death and disaster if the ship were to continue on its intended course. Instead, he advised the ship should make for Mealista island on the south-west coast of Lewis. There, he predicted, they would find a convent of Black Nuns, who had great wealth and would pay well for his wares.[22]

Tostig Godwinson followed the Seer's advice and set a course for Lewis. Nothing further was ever heard of him, his crew or the four remaining chess sets. It has been suggested that these same chessmen would become part of the celebrated hoard that was found in sand dunes in Uig Bay on the Isle of Lewis in a later age, leading to the assumption that the ship was wrecked somewhere off Mealista island south of Uig Bay, and its precious contents buried in the sand for centuries. In support of this contention, Godwinson's cargo comprised four chess sets and so did the famous find of the Lewis chessmen.

The records on Skye of Kenneth Odhar's activities with the Stone are disappointing and incomplete. In one account he heated the Stone and placed it upon a sick man, resulting in a miraculous cure. In others he used the Stone to foretell the weather, to determine whether a pregnant woman would have a male child and even to turn sour milk sweet. It seems improbable that any of these instances would merit a serious accusation of witchcraft or justify the charge that he made use of a stone *being possessed of unnatural and malignant capabilities.* It is for this reason that doubts have been raised as to whether the *malignant* stone of Skye could be the great Stone of Jarl Skule Tostesson. Because of this, some suggest that Kenneth Odhar selected a different and less potent stone when he was offered his choice from the yew box and that the Stone itself remained with Tostig Godwinson's ship. If this were the case, and if his ship were to have been wrecked at Uig, it would offer yet another plausible account of how the Stone first appeared at Baile na Cille.

The further possibility exists that the Stone was carried from Skye to Easter Ross, near Inverness and thence to Loch Ussie on the Brahan estates. In support of this is the letter to Walter Urquhart, Sheriff of Cromarty, penned by a person of substance from Skye. Sections of this have long since been damaged and defaced, ensuring that the identity of the writer remains unknown. The letter related how one Keanoch Owir of Skye, under accusation of witchcraft, had been transported to Easter Ross for trial *together with all evidence of his misdeeds.* This *evidence,* would certainly have included the Stone itself. It is well documented that seven men and twenty-four women were interrogated for witchcraft later that year in Cromarty and that their leader was one Keanoch Owir, curiously described, in a document from Holyroodhouse, as *an enchantress.*

It is possible that this person was the Seer himself. There is no record of a conviction and he would have been released, therefore, at either Dingwall or Strathpeffer. If this thread is followed, it is worth noting that both places are an easy hour's walk from Loch Ussie. Because the Stone was certainly in Loch Ussie at the Brahan Seer's death, and because it may also have been fished from there at an earlier time and removed to Lewis, it is tempting to give this thread special consideration. Although time exists along multiple and tangled strands, some commentators have proposed that there must be a symmetry to account for its turnings. A pleasing idea is that the Seer in an earlier age hid the Stone in Loch Ussie, from whence it was fetched in a different time to empower a later incarnation of the Seer, who once again threw it into Loch Ussie as he was dragged to his death. It is from such symmetries and intricacies that the Celtic knot of time is woven.

On the Nature of Walruses and their Ivory

At one time there were no walruses. They exist as a consequence of a great wrong done by a raven upon an evil spirit, who had himself committed a greater wrong. So it is that walruses are sometimes said to be the result of two great wrongs. An evil spirit had stolen the sun and the moon through a powerful enchantment, thus plunging the world into a darkness terrible beyond imagination. The raven recovered the world's lost light by seducing the spirit's daughter. The father's shame on discovering his daughter had been sullied by a raven caused the spell to loosen and break, returning the sun and moon to their appointed places. The spirit, in a rage, flung his daughter into the sea from the highest cliff in the land. As she fell, she turned into a walrus, her long braids becoming tusks. All walruses are descended from her.

∞

The walrus is a provident source of many useful necessities of life. Its meat is good and slow to spoil, making it the best food for long journeys. Its flippers, when pickled, last through a hard winter. The oil of the walrus burns hot, producing a bright glow, while its hide makes the hardiest ropes. The penis bone makes a fine tent pole, light and strong. A dwelling lined with walrus skin will keep out the fiercest winter gales.

∞

Walruses possess foreknowledge of great disasters, whether they be natural calamities or misfortunes caused by men and war. Greenlanders tell how, on one peaceful afternoon, the walruses left the shore at Bratthlid, swimming away as if pursued in a hunt. Within hours a mighty wave expunged much of the settlement with the loss of many lives. It is well documented that walruses disappear from an area before bouts of plague or pestilence.

∞

When a child is weeping, through pain or distress, the placing of a walrus tusk above its head will cause the tears to cease. This has led some to believe that the tusks are themselves formed from walrus tears and that this accounts for their efficacy.

∞

Walrus ivory is uniquely resistant to spells, whether benign or malicious. This has long been proved by the beneficial power of ivory amulets and tokens, used for many centuries, to ward off sinister spirits and evil magic. It follows from this that a chess set made from walrus ivory cannot be tampered with by magic. In Sweden, where large sums were wagered upon the outcome of chess matches between champions, only those sets carved from walrus ivory could be used in contests. In this way the outcome was free from the influences of magicians.

∞

The northern lights, or *aurora borealis*, are believed among some northern peoples to be a spectral world inhabited by the spirits of any who died by violence. The ever-changing hues of the aurora are caused by the souls of deceased people playing ball games with a walrus head that emits light across every colour of the spectrum. Beyond the far north, this account is disputed, as it is well known that the aurora is caused by the dancing of the White Men (known also as the Merry Dancers or Sky Streamers) who, along with the Fairies and the Blue Men of the Minch, fell to earth with the fallen angels.

∞

The tusk ivory of walruses has long been carved into knives, brooches, clasps and harness pieces. Skilled carvers are highly prized and exalted within their communities. When the Viking Western Greenland settlement disappeared without trace, it was widely believed to have been overrun by Skraelings. But the Skraelings were a generally peaceful people, small of stature, and war, for them, would require a most extreme provocation. An Inuit fisherman told Gunnar Sokkason, who was investigating the cause of the disappearance, that the Skraelings would only embark on a war if their ivory carver had been taken from them by Viking raiders. To kidnap or enslave the ivory carver was as grave an affront as the capture of their king.

∞

When a person is buried, if the grave door is improperly sealed or the funeral ceremony is incorrect in some important detail, the dead person may be transformed into a *draug*. *Drauger* are possessed of great size and heaviness. Despite their weight, they can swim through rock and thus escape from their burial mounds, even though these most substantial of interments should lie under a mountain of stones. *Drauger* wreak revenge on the living who have wronged them in life by sitting upon them at night and suffocating them. If walrus tusks have been interred in the burial mound, the *draug* will take the shape of a walrus. *Drauger* are responsible for many unexplained nocturnal deaths. There is normally no visible sign to detect whether an unexplained death is due to a *draug*. If the spirit takes the form of a walrus, however, it leaves two puncture marks, one at each shoulder of the victim. Most *drauger* can be driven away by spells or powerful runes. Walrus *drauger* are immune to magic and the only prevention is to flee across the sea, for they cannot cross water.

Portents at Brahan

O<small>F ALL THE MYSTERIES SURROUNDING THE STONE,</small> none is more compelling, and none more difficult to explain, than the dark events at Brahan. A lowly labourer, Coinneach Odhar, employed the Stone to become the greatest Seer that Scotland has ever known and then, at the height of his fame, suffered a grisly fate. Parts of this history are familiar to all. For many generations children throughout Scotland have sat wide-eyed, at school and at home, listening to the tales of the Brahan Seer and his prophecies. His predictions have been remarkable, both for their number and their wide-ranging scope. They move from the mundane assurance that a lost sheep will be found, to cataclysmic predictions that great houses will fall or cities be destroyed. Some *seeings* are dire, such as the awful bloodshed at Culloden, while others, like the forecast that horseless carriages would one day pass freely through the glens, are more benign. Many of his predictions have come to pass, despite seeming improbable in the extreme, as instanced by his prophecy that full-rigged ships would pass behind Tomnahurich Hill.[23] This apparently impossible foretelling was fulfilled by the construction of Thomas Telford's mighty Caledonian Canal.

It is not the purpose of this narrative to catalogue or to dwell on the Seer's extraordinary prophecies, for these have been the subject of many books and scholars of great distinction have written much about them. One small area of neglect, in all this writing, however, has been the failure of the learned commentators to observe that a disproportionate number of the Seer's prophecies have involved red-headed women. Moreover, these predictions are generally dark and involve a death:

> *The old bridge at Bonar will go down with a red-headed fishwife on it.*
> *There shall be a laird of Tullock who will kill four wives, but the fifth*
> *shall have red hair and she will kill him.*
> *A pinnacle of rock in Reraig will fall and kill a red-headed woman*
> *and child.*

We may infer, from predictions like these, that the Seer was much occupied with the vexing issue of how his own fate was inextricably entwined with that of a red-headed woman.

An even more significant area of scholarly neglect has been the subtle interactions between Seer and Stone that brought each of the prophecies into being. We know much about them, but little of how they were created. That is the subject of the present chapter.

Even the darkest deed may inadvertently result in some good and, conversely, many a well-intentioned act can lead to unfortunate consequences. When Kenneth Odhar used the Stone to foresee the elevation of Lord Tarbat to the position of Lord Justice General of Scotland, and when his prediction was confirmed as true, there was much rejoicing at Brahan. The Lady Isabella, she of the flaming red hair, ascribed great credit to Kenneth for seeing her father's good fortune and spoke so glowingly of him that his fame began to spread throughout Brahan and beyond. But praise from a high source often brings with it jealousies and carping tongues from envious persons. Before long there were rumours put about that Kenneth Odhar had employed ungodly divinations, and even witchcraft, to make his foresights. Odhar was reputed to be, by nature, a withdrawn and taciturn man who mixed little with other workers on the estate and this fuelled the speculation that there were dark forces informing his predictions.

Kenneth himself, while little disturbed by malevolent whispers, was becoming uneasy for other reasons. The Stone was starting to exert a compulsion on him, not unlike the effect that strong liquor has on those whose moral and mental capacities are unable to resist the wiles of whisky. Each evening, on returning to his cottage from the day's labours, he found himself reaching at once for the Stone. He would derive an inexpressible comfort from the smooth exactness with which it settled into his grasp. And, so strong was the compulsion the Stone had over him, there were many times when he was ravenously hungry but unable to wrench himself from its enticing visions long enough to prepare his food. Sometimes the Stone showed him unfamiliar people and strange events but placed them in a familiar setting. There was an exotically dressed tall man wearing a high hat, pacing up and down in deep thought along the shore of Loch Ussie, where Kenneth himself often walked; or he saw a child he did not know, sitting outside his cottage playing with purple pebbles. Then there were the strange landscapes where nothing was recognisable to him; red and black hills scarred as if a great fire had passed across them, or a city of silver and glass where strangely garbed people moved so fast that their faces were blurred. Sometimes the Stone showed him a complete life story: once he saw a baby born, grow into a strapping young man, marry his sweetheart, raise a family and drown at sea all within the space of an hour's seeing. At other times, the Stone eavesdropped on inconsequential conversations. Kenneth found these varied visions compelling, but sometimes now he worried that the Stone was starting to exert an irresistible control over him.

One Sunday, the sermon at Kintail church was to be preached by John MacRae, minister of Dingwall, the son of Reverend Farquhar

MacRae, who had been Kenneth's teacher when he first arrived on the Brahan estate from Lewis. Kenneth Odhar had heard the preacher before and, like the other churchgoers from the estate, knew to expect a lengthy homily on the evils of drunkenness. It was perhaps for this reason that many of the estate labourers, forewarned, skulked in the pews at the back of the congregation, trying to hide their rheumy Saturday-night eyes and red noses from the piercing gaze of John MacRae. On entering the church, and finding no seats left in the rear pews, Kenneth was forced to seat himself at the front right under the preacher's accusing glare.

As anticipated, John MacRae waxed long and eloquent on the multitude of evils that indulgence brought to both drinkers and those around them. Kenneth, as a sober man, was well able to withstand the preacher's steely eye and looked back at the pulpit with an expression of calm innocence. Then, unexpectedly, the sermon took a new course. Looking directly at Kenneth, the Reverend MacRae spoke with great sternness: "There may be those amongst us today," he warned, "who are free from the demons of drink and who believe my condemnation of indulgence does not encompass them. But any indulgence whatsoever, any excess, is a sin, whether it be gluttony or another unbridled compulsion. We must all strive against the snares of immoderation."

Kenneth felt himself redden and found that he was unable to return the preacher's gaze. He imagined that the whole kirk was watching him and he was acutely conscious of the Stone, nestled deeply within his pouch. On returning to his cottage, he vowed to use it no more. At first, the strength of his intention prevailed over his fascination with the strange worlds that the Stone revealed to him. Because he was afflicted with the second sight, inherited from his mother, he could still sense future events without using the Stone. In fact, the second sight had developed so strongly within him during recent years that many of his prophecies and prognostications had been made without even raising the Stone to his eye. Being unsure which parts of his seeings were due to his second sight and which were due to the Stone, Kenneth was not surprised when his visions continued, even though he had concealed the Stone beneath his bed. To be certain, however, that the Stone was not still reaching out to influence his mind, he decided to hide it in a place of greater remoteness. He knew, from his mother, that wells were the most secret and secure places to conceal seeing stones, being opaque both to magic and to the second sight. Kenneth's own early experiences as a well digger had given him a deep respect for wells and their powers. He feared that should the Stone offend or sully a well by its presence, he himself would be the victim of perpetual misfortune. After much thought, he decided instead to hide the Stone within an abandoned stone water trough, near one of the burnt mounds where, in former times, women had assembled for communal cooking.[24] In so doing, he believed that the Stone would no longer be able to exert any excessive influence upon his thoughts. When he reached the trough he found that it was half filled with murky water. He tested the depth of the water with a stick and found that it was nowhere deeper than his elbow. Taking the Stone from his purse he held it in his hand for one last time, running his fingers along its seductive smoothness. Then, almost casually, he dropped it into the trough, letting the dark water enfold it. Kenneth waited for a minute until the ripples he had created subsided, first into wrinkles and then into a stagnant stillness. Turning on his heel, he went home.

For several weeks, his stratagem appeared to be successful. The compulsion to grasp and use the Stone diminished somewhat, although his second sight remained unaffected. It was this second sight that presented him one morning with a troubling vision. Kenneth was crossing behind one of the estate barns when he saw a woman in a hooded white cloak coming towards him. He stopped and stood respectfully aside, for she was well dressed and had the bearing of a lady of substance. As she drew level with him, she pulled back her white hood, revealing a head of long reddish hair. Kenneth was thrown into confusion. The woman looked like the Lady Isabella, but her face was different in some small ways and her hair less vibrant. His awkwardness with strangers, particularly with women, caused him to lower his eyes for an instant. When he looked up, she was no longer there. He realised at once that he had seen an apparition.

The next day, Kenneth was sent to collect a scythe from the smithy at Kintail. He returned across the fields to Brahan, trudging with the scythe over his shoulder, an unwitting likeness of the images of death chiselled upon tombstones in the old churchyard at Dingwall. He was deep in thought, debating with himself as to whether the Stone was indeed the *unbridled compulsion* and *snare of immoderation* that the Reverend MacRae had so fiercely preached against. It was true, he conceded, that he had sometimes spent time with the Stone to the exclusion of other activities. But it was equally true that he had used the Stone for good. He had employed it to find the treasured ring that the Lady Isabella had lost and, in doing so, had saved her maid from unjust accusation. He had used the Stone to warn of several future disasters in time to avert them. On the night when the Old Stables at Beauly collapsed, neither horses nor grooms were hurt, all were sleeping elsewhere, forewarned by his timely prediction. Yet his conscience continued to trouble him. All those compelling hours spent with the Stone at his eye might have been used to better purpose.

The more Kenneth pondered, the deeper he became entangled in indecision. He continued his walk towards Brahan with a stooping gait, oblivious of his surroundings, his mind absorbed in issues beyond his capacity to resolve. In consequence of his inner turmoil, he failed to see the apparition until he was almost upon it. He started back in surprise, almost dropping the scythe. The spirit woman appeared grimly amused by his discomfiture.

"It is fitting we meet again," she said, speaking in a refined tone that betrayed her aristocratic lineage. "Bearing your scythe, you look to be the very effigy of death and it is of death that I must speak."

"Death? Who are you? Why do you appear to me?"

"I am from another time. I am the last of the Seaforth MacKenzie women to be born. After me our line will be extinguished as a consequence of a dire prophecy that you will make."

Kenneth stammered in confusion, his mind reeling with questions. "Prophecy? How could I predict ill to the MacKenzies who have given me shelter and succour since I was but a bairn?"

"Aye, but that you surely will. You will speak in malice and, in the doing of it, you will bring about the destruction of the House of Seaforth. History will record that you made a vile augury of early deaths, pestilence, blindness, suffering and poverty for the Seaforths. I am the sister of Lady Caroline MacKenzie, last of the Seaforth line, she whom you prophesied would die by her sister's hand. I am the *white-hooded lassie from the east* who, in your malediction will kill her sister and I have now come to make my revenge through a prophecy in return. Hark well, Coinneach Odhar, for this is your fate. The day that you are parted from your cursed Stone shall be the day that you die a terrible death. I can neither change nor subvert the consequences of your ill predictions and neither can you change mine. When you part from the Stone that killed my line, then shall your own life be forfeit."

Before Kenneth could collect his wits, the apparition had melted away, leaving him dazed and leaning on the scythe shaft for support. He stumbled back to his cottage and sat shaking in the gathering dusk. His mind was in a ferment. His mother had told him how the spectral princess at Baile na Cille had warned her he risked death at the hand of a red-headed woman; now his death was to be a consequence of separation from the Stone. He spent a sleepless night, tossing in mounting unease, but by morning he had resolved nothing. He arose full of confusion and without any intention or action in his head. Few of the decisions on which our lives hinge are made through reason and clear thought. They come, instead, in moments of certainty that defy all analysis. So it was with Kenneth Odhar. As he set out that morning, bleary-eyed to his labours, it was suddenly clear to him what he must do. He made straight for the stone water trough at the burnt mound where he had hidden the Stone. He knew beyond doubt that his only course now was to retrieve the Stone and to keep it with him at all times. Reaching his arm deep into the cold and murky waters of the trough, he let his fingers run along the bottom in search of the concealed pebble. A slow panic washed over him and his blood turned colder than the trough water. Kenneth Odhar found that he could not breathe. The Seeing Stone of Brahan was not there.

The Seer's Parting

A
S THE SEER'S FINGERS TRAWLED frantically through the frigid water of the trough and came up with nothing, he felt his whole world plummet into blackness. The Stone was gone. He plunged both his hands into the chill murk and scraped along the rough bottom of the trough, searching and searching until his fingers bled. Kenneth Odhar struggled to focus his eyes and his heart was gripped by the icy certainty that the death prophecy of the red-headed woman, the last of the Seaforth MacKenzie line, was about to be fulfilled. The cold fury of her voice echoed in his ears: "The day you are parted from your cursed Stone shall be the day you die a terrible death." He flung himself to the ground, berating his own stupidity. How could he have dropped the Stone so readily into this fetid water?

Kenneth Odhar was so absorbed in his search for the Stone and in his subsequent self-recrimination that he failed to notice an old woman dressed in black, squatting at a slab nearby. She had been pounding grain to make gruel, placing a mixture of oats and corn in a depression in the slab and then pummelling and grinding them with a pebble, but had paused in her labours when she first saw him approach the trough. The woman was the widow of the estate's stonemason and, through her late husband, she had

177

come to know Kenneth a little better than most who lived there. She waited silently, watching him. After a while, caught in the uncomfortable position of seeing a man in such sore distress, she decided to resume her grinding. At the sound of her pounding, Kenneth struggled to collect himself. He rose to his feet. His first thought was to slink away, pretending that the lack of control he had exhibited had never taken place. He looked closely at the old woman, trying to assess whether she, too, would choose to forget his unseemly display, or whether the incident was destined to become estate gossip. It was then that he noticed the pebble she was using to pound her grains. It was pale and, although the better part of it was concealed in her hand, it was unquestionably the Stone, *his* Stone. Kenneth was overcome with a joyous relief so profound that it racked his whole being.

"Whence came that stone you use?" he demanded.

"I pulled water from the trough and found it in my bucket."

"It is mine and I shall reward you well for its return." So saying, he took a silver groat from his purse. "My one requirement is that we do not speak again of what happened here."

The old woman willingly assented. The coin was a substantial sum for an estate widow and very welcome to one in her reduced circumstances.

Kenneth took the Stone from her and nestled it into his palm, where it rested with a comfortable familiarity. He turned it over and examined every part of its surface carefully, finding no damage or detriment, despite its recent hard use. Returning to his cottage he was overwhelmed by tiredness from the twin effects of loss and unexpected rediscovery. In consequence, he lapsed into a fitful stupor and fell asleep where he sat, with the Stone in his hand. He dreamed that the Reverend John MacRae was sitting with him on the shore of Loch Ussie, on a grassy knoll that was Kenneth's favourite place for moments of quiet contemplation.

"I fear that the Stone may exert over me the *unbridled compulsion* of which you spoke disapprovingly in your sermon," he ventured. "Yet I have certain knowledge that I shall die if parted from it."

MacRae, unexpectedly, offered him words of comfort. "Excess and indulgence are sinful when they lead to ill effects." He paused. "But there is no such thing as excessive good, or excessive truth. If you use your stone for the good of others, and not for the advancement of yourself, I can see no objection provided that you always speak truthfully." In his dream, Kenneth was suffused with contentment and, in a dream within a dream, imagined himself falling into restful sleep on the bank of the loch.

When he awoke, he was sitting in his cottage, the Stone still clasped in his hand. Darkness was easing into the early grey of dawn. He realised that he had slept not only most of the day but also through the ensuing night. His mouth was dry so, stretching the stiffness from his limbs, he poured himself a cup of water from his pitcher. As he drained it he felt a new peace and a new certainty of purpose. He breakfasted cheerfully upon a stale loaf and, putting the Stone into his purse, departed for his usual day of labour on the estate. Scarcely had he progressed a hundred steps when the Earl of Seaforth's factor came riding up to him. The factor was a grave grey-bearded man, formal in the old manner.

"Our master, Lord Kenneth of Kintail, Third Earl of Seaforth, Chief of Clan MacKenzie, commands your presence at noon in Brahan castle Great Hall," he said, with all the solemn gravity of one pronouncing a death sentence. Without waiting for a response, he turned his horse and was gone in a clatter of hooves. Under normal circumstances, Kenneth would have been filled with dread at such a summons. Today, however, he felt only anticipation and a suppressed excitement. The Laird's summons gave him an absolute excuse for a day's absence from estate labouring and, as he had three hours before his required appearance, he returned to his cottage, changed into his best clothes and made his way to the

179

grassy knoll on the Loch Ussie shore where he had dreamed his conversation with the Reverend MacRae had taken place. While he sat there, Kenneth Odhar debated whether he should employ the Stone to see the substance and outcome of his meeting with the Earl. It could be argued that to do so would be to use the Stone to his personal advantage, which MacRae had forbidden. MacRae had also said, however, that the Stone was to be used in the pursuit of truth and that purpose appeared to Kenneth to provide the stronger argument. Raising the Stone to his eye for the first time in many weeks, he sought sight of his own future. He saw the Earl running towards the estate stables calling out to the grooms, "Bring me my fastest horse for I must ride like the wind to save Kenneth Odhar. He has served me well and I must now serve him." Then the image faded and Kenneth could see nothing through the Stone's aperture except the placid waters of Loch Ussie.

At first he was unsure how to interpret this fragment of the future. After some reflection, he decided that it presaged well for him. The Earl was clearly most satisfied with his service and, remarkably, was prepared to exert himself considerably on Kenneth's behalf. So, as noon approached, the Seer entered Brahan's Great Hall with confidence. The Earl greeted him with more cordiality than would normally be accorded to an estate labourer.

"Your fame extends beyond Brahan," he said. "I hear well of the accuracy and acuteness of your predictions. My wife, the Lady Isabella, has related to me the occasion when you made a telling for her. You foresaw that her father, Lord Tarbat, would receive the King's pardon and become Lord Justice General of Scotland. In this matter you were most prescient."

Kenneth waited patiently, unsure of where the Earl was leading him.

"I have a question for you: a matter that runs beyond idle curiosity," the Earl said, lowering his voice so that none could hear his words. "Is it so that you can see distant events, even those that will take place upon foreign soil?"

"I have not frequently had reason to look upon far distant occurrences," Kenneth replied, "but I have often seen events in Inverness and beyond. I do not believe distance hinders the Stone's power."

"In that case," said the Earl, his voice dropping to a whisper, "I may wish to employ you to assist in a delicate matter of State. This means I must reveal to you matters of a sensitive nature. Do I have your oath that you will serve me alone and maintain close silence over all that I may henceforward tell you in secrecy?"

"You have my oath."

"Then your station within my employment shall be improved. You are to live in a room within the castle and you shall serve me as my ..."

The Earl paused while he searched for a word.

"In former days, I might have said 'necromancer' but in these modern times men have been burned as witches for less. Perhaps you should be my Seer." He thought for a moment. "Yes. I confer upon you the title of the Brahan Seer and it is under that name that you will henceforth be known."

Kenneth was finding it difficult to digest the Earl's words. "What is it that you require of me, my Lord?" he asked cautiously, thinking this sudden advance in his fortunes could not come without some considerable cost.

The Earl ignored his question. "How can I be certain that your stone can see events on foreign soil?"

"I saw Lord Tarbat speaking with men in a far land," said Kenneth, meaning England, a place that was as far off to him as China, "but I was enabled in that seeing. Her Ladyship permitted me to hold Lord Tarbat's ring."

"Do you suppose," the Earl asked, "that you could do the same with a glove or some other article of a person's attire?"

"I believe so, my Lord."

"Then I shall reveal more to you of my main purpose. I am engaged upon a matter of some gravity concerning a highborn lady who had the acquaintance of a great royal personage while he was in France. It is his desire to know the disposition of this lady and it is my hope to be of service to His Highness in the fulfilment of his intentions. I am summoned to London to confer upon the matter and I shall endeavour to return with possessions or articles of her clothing such that you can perform a seeing to further our purpose."

The Earl thought for a moment.

"I will be away a month or more. Meanwhile I shall announce your position as the Brahan Seer and you shall devote your whole time to the business of divination on behalf of our estate. Do I have your assent?"

Remembering the words of Reverend MacRae in his dream, Kenneth nodded. "I must use the Stone to do good and to tell truth," he replied.

The Earl laughed. "In matters of State, truth is more flexible than a willow branch and more slippery than January ice. Be careful, my friend, that truth does not slide from beneath you and cause you to fall."

And, so saying, he dismissed Kenneth and prepared himself for his trip south.

Because the title of Brahan Seer had been conferred upon him by no less a person than the Earl of Seaforth, Head of the Clan MacKenzie, Kenneth Odhar gained both legitimacy in the eyes of his contemporaries and a consequent degree of notoriety. He was moved from his humble cottage to a room in the castle, prepared for him by order of the Earl. The factor, who was responsible for carrying out the Earl's wishes in this respect, chose to give

Kenneth a mean room in the lower part of the castle which was normally used as a holding cell for felons awaiting judgment. It had one small barred window and a stout door with an impressive but rusty iron lock. If the factor had hoped to slight Kenneth by this action, he was to be disappointed. The Seer was delighted by his new lodging, for it was within the castle itself and a mark of privilege. His only cause for complaint was that the lock was so rusty that it took two men to turn the key. He soon, however, found that the door could be opened, even when locked, by the simple expedient of lifting it slightly so that it unlatched. He was in every way highly contented with his new position and his living arrangements.

People who would at one time have feared to seek a prediction from him in case there might be some taint of witchcraft, now openly sought his advice and counsel. As a result Kenneth received a constant stream of supplicants from the estate and beyond. Even Reverend MacRae journeyed from his parish at Dingwall to ask him for help in finding two silver chalices that were missing from his church.

In MacRae's presence, Kenneth raised the Stone to his eye, an action he would never have dared before his newfound recognition and title. "You shall find the chalices hidden in Strathpeffer under thatch in the roof of a house owned by John Collins," he told the preacher, "although he is not the man who took them." Then he added, "But little good will it do you, for though you keep them under lock and key, they will again disappear one year hence and they shall never more be found."

MacRae was clearly shaken by the detail of the Seer's prophecy and by the calm assurance with which it had been made, but he quickly regained his composure.

"I thank you for this information," he said gravely. "The Stone you hold has great power. I must advise you to use it only in the pursuit of good and to ever use it truthfully." It was now the Seer's turn to be startled, for the Reverend MacRae had spoken to him exactly as he had done in his dream.

"You may rest content," the Seer assured him, "that I shall give absolute heed to your words and I shall let them guide my every action with this Stone."

During the month that the Earl sojourned in London, Kenneth had many opportunities to explore the intricacies of prophecy using the Stone. Evenings provided clearer insights than mornings, for example, and this the Seer ascribed to his weariness at night making him a passive receptacle for the Stone's sights. He learned to free his mind from all presuppositions and, as a result, the clarity of his seeings improved. He learned the knack of prompting the Stone with subtle suggestion. The Stone was perverse in this matter. If the Seer's interest appeared too direct, or his need too urgent, the Stone seemed to take a delight in thwarting him. When the daughter of the estate's seedsman was missing, Kenneth's impatience for a vision, his urgency prompted by agitated parents, so upset the Stone that it refused to grant him any sight whatsoever. There was a palpable resistance, almost an antagonism, from the Stone that made it difficult even to hold it up to his eye. Yet, when the distraught parents had left to seek more responsive help elsewhere, the Stone responded with eagerness and he could instantly see the child playing safely with her cousins not a mile away.

As the Seer gained mastery over the subtle ways of the Stone, he found the confidence to issue foretellings encompassing every dimension of time and place. He saw events that were fulfilled within minutes of his prediction and, at the other extreme, far off future happenings that would come to pass many centuries hence. He also learned to express his visions in a particular voice that lay somewhere between a chant and a bardic verse. Contemporary accounts say that he entered a trance-like state and intoned his prophecies as if partly asleep. Others wrote down what he said and their reporting of his words provides the record of his prophecies that exists today. At times he entered into an ecstatic condition, where his eyelids fluttered, his breathing became shallow and his speech so rapid that few could follow its pace or meaning. It is certain that many important foretellings were lost because they were issued too rapidly for accurate transcription.

When the Earl returned from London he found a Seer transformed. There was little trace left of the diffident and bashful Kenneth Odhar, labourer of Brahan. In the short space of a single month, the Seer had become more forceful and confident in his demeanour. The only sign of his former shyness was in the presence of women, when he exhibited awkwardness and an inability to look directly at them. The Earl, within half an hour of stepping from his coach, had summoned the Seer for consultations, much to the displeasure of the Countess Isabella, who had expected that – after a month's absence – she alone would occupy her husband's thoughts and desires. Closeted with the Seer, the Earl again swore him to secrecy.

"I shall reveal to you a matter of State and warn you that it would be high treason to divulge what I shall now tell you."

The Earl reached into his pouch and drew from it a lady's glove, made from the most delicate kidskin and bearing an intricately embroidered letter 'M'.

"The lady whose glove this is holds certain items; particular letters and tokens. Should these items be misused, the consequences to the State, and to several of our highest and most noble personages, would be dire. It does not extend the truth to say that the very monarchy might be endangered. I have undertaken the assignment to procure their recovery and, in that matter, I must rely on your seeings. It is certain that these items will be artfully concealed, for there is little doubt that the lady knows well the import of what she holds."

Kenneth picked up the glove and held it in his left hand for a long time. He drew the Stone from his purse and, with his right hand, raised it to his eye. After what seemed an eternity to the Earl, the Seer lowered his Stone.

"I see nothing."

"Try once more," the Earl urged him.

They spent a fruitless hour attempting a sighting but the Stone would not comply. The Seer tried every artifice. He tempted the Stone by first asking for simple everyday visions so straightforward that it had always instantly proffered them to him before. There was no response. Kenneth placed the glove in contact with the Stone; he even slipped the Stone inside the glove. Finally, in great anxiety, he asked the Earl to let him go alone with the glove to the grassy spot on the shore of Loch Ussie, where he had many times made powerful foretellings. As he reached the loch, dusk was creeping across Brahan. With scant hope of a seeing, he set the Stone to his eye and, to his astonishment, beheld a luminous tableau. It was not unlike a picture of the stage of a grand theatre in Edinburgh that he had once been shown in a book by his teacher, the Reverend Farquhar MacRae. There were no persons present upon this stage and Kenneth was perplexed by what he saw. Then he had a sudden apprehension: this was not a stage at all; it was a resplendently ornate room. He had never seen anything so imposing in his life, for the Great Hall at Brahan castle, the grandest place he knew, was starkly plain in comparison. The walls and the ceiling of this palatial chamber were a rich green and heavily gilded with intricate decoration. There were six sparkling candelabra, each holding a hundred candles or more. Three intricately crafted wooden panels further adorned one wall of the room, the middle panel being of a rich wood inlaid with ivory and depicting a hunting scene. On one side of this central panel was a small bronze statue, set into the wall, of a huntsman blowing his horn in triumph.

The Seer was so transfixed by this vision that he lost all sense of time. When he came to his senses it was dark and, he guessed from the chill in the air, past midnight. He returned to his room in the castle to find the Earl of Seaforth's factor awaiting him. The man regarded the Seer with disapproval.

"Lord Kenneth of Kintail, Third Earl of Seaforth, Chief of Clan MacKenzie has waited many hours for your reappearance," he admonished. "You will appear before him in his private chamber at dawn."

An hour before dawn, waiting in the Earl's antechamber, the Seer ventured another seeing. Through the Stone's aperture he saw the same grand room, although it was now late evening. The imposing candelabra were unlit and parts of the room were deep in shadow. The Seer could make out no movement, yet he sensed a presence in the room. He knew the Stone too well to display an open interest and so he waited patiently until it was ready to show him more. After some minutes he saw an exquisitely dressed woman emerge from the shadows. She crept towards the central panel, that which was decorated with the ivory hunting scene, while furtively glancing behind her. Seeming assured that she was unobserved, she grasped the hunting horn on the bronze statue and twisted it. Kenneth Odhar watched in astonishment as the panel slid aside, to reveal a small shelf containing a bundle of documents and letters tied with a ribbon. The lady reached out her hand and touched the bundle. Then, apparently satisfied, she twisted the hunting horn to its original position. The panel slid back into place and the woman moved silently from the room.

Kenneth was uncertain as to the meaning of this vision but, less than an hour later, when he described it to the Earl, Lord Seaforth immediately comprehended the significance of what the Seer told him.

"It is unquestionably her hiding place," he mused, "and it should make recovery of the letters a simple matter. Moreover, from descriptions of her family palace in Paris given to me by the royal personage who has entrusted me with this enterprise, the

187

room must be the Grand Salon itself."

The Earl professed himself highly contented with his Seer's work. Calling the factor, he instructed him immediately to pay the Brahan Seer the princely sum of five guineas. On hearing the Earl's instruction, the grey-bearded factor was clearly displeased and seemed reluctant to fetch the money from the castle treasury.

"Bring it without delay," the Earl instructed him, with some irritation, "for he is the Seer of Brahan and he has today done me a service greater than any that ever I have received from you."

The Earl left to prepare for his mission to Paris, so that Kenneth was alone in the antechamber when the factor returned.

"Here is your money," he hissed, tossing the five guineas to the floor at the Seer's feet. "But mark my words, you will suffer for bewitching my Lord and turning him against me. My family has served the Seaforths since the first Earl was but a bairn and no vulgar labouring man shall supplant us through enchantments and witchcraft. Sorcery is a dangerous game that will lead you inexorably to the fire." He turned on his heel, leaving Kenneth to pick up the five golden guineas from the floor.

The Seer was little troubled by the factor's words. It is in the nature of great estates that servants at every level are awash in currents of pettiness and jealousy. He told himself that such an untoward reaction from the factor was natural and would soon pass. It was for this reason that the Seer was not alarmed when the Stone began, frequently, to show him visions of the factor whispering in the ear of the Lady Isabella. He suspected no malice, even when, two weeks later, he received a perfunctory summons from the factor to appear before her ladyship. Lady Isabella was seated in the Great Hall, surrounded by her ladies and the leaders of the estate, with the Earl's factor at her side. Again, Kenneth saw nothing amiss, for the factor, as the legal representative of the Brahan estate, was habitually and necessarily in the presence of the Earl and his Lady.

Isabella appeared agitated. She leaned towards the factor and the two of them whispered for a long time. Smoothing back a tendril of her glowing hair she finally turned back to the Seer.

"An accusation has been made against you," she told him. "It is a serious matter. Our closest advisers suspect you of witchcraft and sorcery. I am caught here by unfortunate circumstances. The Lord Seaforth himself would customarily hear such a serious charge against a member of our estate at Brahan and this matter should await his return. But, alas, it cannot. The accusation against you is that my Lord's absence in Paris is at your behest. It is said that he has been lured there by you to meet a woman and that you have cast a spell to enthrall and imprison him there."

The factor again whispered something in Lady Isabella's ear. "The issue is this," she continued. "Whilst he is held by your enchantment he can never return and, if we follow custom, you will never face his inquiry and justice. So I must, in his absence, enquire into this matter myself."

Kenneth was dumbstruck. All the newfound confidence that came with his title of the Brahan Seer deserted him. He struggled to put into words some defence against his accusers.

"My Lady, have I not served you and the Seaforths well?"

"That you have," Isabella conceded.

"And in the matter of Lord Tarbat's happy news, was I not the bearer?"

"That you were, and for that very same reason it is my hope you can give an account of yourself to show that this whole affair is based on an unfortunate misunderstanding."

"I am the cause of nothing," the Seer stammered. "It was the Reverend MacRae who instructed me: 'Tell only truth with the Stone,' he said, 'and do only good'. That I have done and naught more."

"Then instruct me as to the matter of my husband. Was it not you and your stone that sent him to Paris? Where is the good in that? Why did you send him there?"

Kenneth considered his best reply. His oath of secrecy to the Earl meant that he was unable to reveal any part of Lord Seaforth's quest. It was suddenly clear to the Seer that the Earl had told nobody else at Brahan of his purpose, not even his own lady. Being under the oath, he was unable to explain.

"I cannot answer you."

Here the factor spoke.

"Then I shall answer for this base enchanter. He used his stone to entice our Lord. I heard some words between them. The wizard ... no, let me put it plainly ... this witch, this occult dealer with the devil, he spoke to the Lord Seaforth of a woman in Paris. Within the hour, the Earl was preparing to leave to meet her as if under a compulsion or irresistible spell."

Isabella's face was white and her red hair seemed to spark light. "How do you answer this?" she demanded.

Kenneth remained silent, bound by his vow of secrecy.

"Is it true he is with a woman in Paris, even as we speak?"

"I cannot tell you. I do not know what he does at this moment."

"Then use your stone to discern it, for although I have little liking for the accusations against you, I like your answers even less."

At first Kenneth Odhar demurred but, seeing the gravity of the situation, and realising for the first time that his very life was at risk, he finally agreed to a seeing. Raising the Stone to his eye he fervently hoped to see nothing or perhaps only to see something inconsequential. Instead the Stone revealed to him the Earl in conversation with an elegant lady dressed in fine clothing. Then, before he could lower it, it further showed the Earl in the Grand Salon, removing the packet of documents from their hiding place. The Earl was smiling with great satisfaction as he closed the secret compartment and swiftly left the room.

"Did you see him with the woman?" Isabella quizzed him.

Mindful of his promise to MacRae to tell only the truth from his seeings, Kenneth nodded.

"Well," she insisted, "this requires answer beyond a mere nod. What manner of woman? Describe her exactly."

"She is a woman of great beauty, wearing a graceful green dress," replied the unhappy Seer. He could hear gasps and murmurs from the estate ladies who had been watching the entire proceedings most intently.

Isabella was visibly angered by Kenneth's reply but that anger paled in comparison to the fury that shook her frame when she heard the titters of the women around her. Barely maintaining her composure she asked a final question.

"And what is my Lord's disposition? Is he happy with the situation that you have contrived for him?"

The Seer had no choice. "He is greatly content," he replied, "I saw him smiling with happiness as he held that which he most desired."

Loud gasps went around the hall. Isabella's fury now knew no bounds.

"You shall burn for this," she screamed. "You have defamed my Lord, the Chief of the Clan MacKenzie and you have done so in the presence of his vassals."

The factor was ready with his men. They seized Kenneth Odhar and dragged him back to his cell, where, with great effort, they turned the key in the rusty lock to imprison him. The rapid turn of events had left the Seer disconcerted and confused. It was some hours before he realized that he had been through a trial of sorts and had been condemned to burn as a witch. He sought counsel, using the Stone, but no vision was forthcoming. Gathering his wits, he decided that it would be fatal to remain here in the hands of the factor and his men. He waited until nightfall and then, by lifting the door from its latch, he was able to escape from the castle under cover of darkness. He made for the burnt mounds around Loch Ussie and there he hid for two days. During this concealment, there were many times when he attempted to entice a vision from the Stone but without success. He slowly came to understand that the Stone had deserted him.

On the third day, the Seer heard the sounds of a large group of men and dogs in the distance and knew that there was no escape. He was apprehended and taken back to the castle in readiness for transportation to Chanonry, on the Black Isle, where he was to be executed. As he was being dragged along the shore of Loch Ussie Kenneth Odhar struggled free and flung the Stone deep into the loch. In a mighty voice he cursed the Stone and prophesied that it would lie there until it would be discovered in the belly of a fish and that it would bring misfortune to one who would become a seer as great as himself.[25]

The Seer was taken to Chanonry and it was there he learned his fate. The particulars of how he was burned as a witch in a barrel of flaming tar have been recounted thousands of times and there is little purpose in elaborating them here. Suffice it to say that few have ever suffered a more painful or more unjust end than that of the Brahan Seer. It is fitting that, as he was being dragged to the fire, he made his final prophecy, the downfall of the House of Seaforth, and that this prophecy has come to pass in every exact and unfortunate detail.

As the Seer was being taken to Chanonry for execution, the Earl of Seaforth returned to Brahan unexpectedly from Paris. Instantly realising the manifest injustice that was impending, the Earl saddled his fastest steed and rode like the wind to prevent the execution. He arrived too late. All this, and the gruesome details of the Seer's burning in a barrel of tar, have become accepted truths, refined through many generations of telling. The monument to the Brahan Seer, that stands today at Chanonry Point, commemorates these events and testifies to the power and the endurance of the story of Kenneth Odhar.

But what of the Stone? Flung from the Seer's hand, it looped and twisted down into the chill depths of Loch Ussie. Once there, it completed one journey, the most famous of its many threads, and awaited the next. It had moved through time itself, and would soon move again; it would twist along its intricate path like the convolutions of a Celtic knot, before returning once more to Baile na Cille. It is there that the silver thread of time causes events to spiral back upon themselves in loops that may be never-ending. Baile na Cille is a place of magic, that lies at the nexus of a great knot where time and legend merge and jostle fretfully like the sea. It is fitting that it is to the pool there that the Stone should always return.

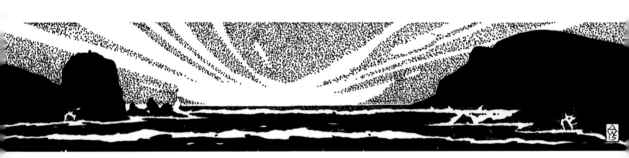

On the Nature of the Penalties of Foretelling

The timeline on which our world exists proceeds at an inexorable and even pace. It cannot be halted, it cannot be slowed, it cannot be hastened. Yet, under certain circumstances, it can be bypassed through mechanisms that enable a future to be seen. These mechanisms are, without exception, unnatural. Seeing into the future – whether by runes, seeing stones, divinations, magic or witchcraft – violates the natural order of time. Those who have deeply studied the nature of time agree that such violations will rarely go unpunished, and that those who dabble in divination will often suffer penalties for their temerity.

∞

Sometimes it is hard to discern whether retribution for foretelling the future results from the character of unnatural prophecy itself or whether from an altercation between stone and seer. It has been widely noted that shortly before a penalty is exacted from the seer there often occurs some matter or event through which stone and seer are set at odds. A month before Isabel Goudie was arraigned in Auldern for witchcraft, she had thrown her stone into the fire, saying that it was an ill thing and she was well rid of it.

∞

A further example of this difficulty may be found in the tale of Martin MacLeod of Horgabost, who possessed a powerful stone that he found on the shore of Loch Seaforth. MacLeod was an ambitious man and used his stone to foresee ways in which he might enrich himself, often at the expense of his neighbours.

He amassed much wealth in this way, through seeing events before their time. Such was the antagonism he aroused that he was brought before the kirk to make confession of his acts. Fearing that he would be accused of witchcraft, he agreed never to use his stone again and so he flung it into the sea. No sooner had the stone disappeared beneath the surface than a great wave came up and swept him to his death. For many years afterwards there was fierce argument about whether his death was retribution for seeing the future or whether it was revenge caused by his stone for its repudiation.

∞

Retribution for foretelling may be exacted by a stone's gift of false visions. Mathew McKinnon of Beauly inherited a seeing stone from his father that had a reputation for infallibility. For over forty years his stone's foretellings had invariably proved accurate and there had not been a single exception to this rule. Mathew made a seeing in which the old stone toll bridge at Nairn collapsed and took four lives with it. He rushed to warn the folk of Nairn, expecting to be thanked for his pains. Instead he found himself confronted by the toll bridge owner who was enraged and berated Mathew for promulgating wild rumours that put at risk his lucrative toll business. The owner offered to make a wager of one hundred pounds to be paid, should the bridge fall within a year. Mathew readily accepted the bet, thinking it easy money, as his stone had not proved wrong in forty years. After a year, with the bridge still intact, Mathew was forced to pay the wager, throwing himself and his family into penury. This instance has been used to prove that the very nature of foreseeing brings with it an inevitable retribution, and that even forty years of successful prediction must ultimately exact a heavy cost. Others have suggested that Mathew McKinnon's ruin was not the result of meddling with the unnatural act of seeing but occurred solely because he had slighted his stone in some way.

∞

A stone will normally exact retribution for seeing the future only from the seer who has looked through it. There have been credible instances reported, however, when a stone has punished an individual who has not directly used it. An instance is the Harris merchant who, with his sister, visited Inverness several times each year and transacted business there that made him wealthy. After one such occasion, on their return from Inverness, the merchant was smitten with permanent blindness. His sister confessed then that their visits to Inverness had in truth been to indulge secretly in gambling. Her brother had forced her to use a stone that had belonged to their grandfather, to see the outcome of events in order that they might wager and be sure to win. Because their grandfather had been struck blind after looking through the stone, the merchant had refused to use it himself but forced his sister to foretell the outcome of wagers on his behalf. This she did, although unwillingly and with much weeping. The stone spared her the penalty but justly exacted it from her brother.

∞

Many who have long acquaintance with seeing stones believe that misfortunes from foretelling are not due to retribution for altering the natural

sequence of time but always result from malice in the stone itself. They argue that by treating a stone with great deference and respect, misfortune will never come to the seer. As proof of this, they instance the Hermit of Schiehallion, who kept a stone for fifty years without mishap. The Hermit insisted that every supplicant who came seeking a prediction should bring a vial of seawater to bathe the stone. He spoke kind and respectful words to it before raising it to his eye and kept it in a place of high honour in his cell.

∞

A court at Chanonry, held under commissions of justiciary, heard a witchcraft charge brought against one John Glass. There was a compelling case against him for sorcery using seeing stones to foretell all manner of things. At first it seemed he was destined to be burned as a witch, but the justices gave him reprieve, noting that all prophecies he had made were universally benign and resulted in no ill to anyone. This is a rare instance of a seer escaping penalty for the temerity of foreseeing.

∞

Thomas Blacklock, who had been blind since birth, made many successful predictions that he ascribed to his second sight. He was a man of rude health and robust constitution. He developed a severe tremor in his left hand, although all other parts of his person were unaffected. He consulted a famous surgeon in Edinburgh and confided to him that he believed the tremor to be a punishment inflicted upon him by a seeing stone that he had secretly been using for many years to make his foretellings.

The Return to Baile na Cille

THE TELLING OF STONES IS A NECKLACE made from multiple strings. Each string is an account of the Stone's movement from place to place and across time. Some strings are pure legend, while others are based on historic fact. Like a necklace, the two ends of the tale's strands are joined together at the clasp, so that ends become beginnings. The pool at Baile na Cille, where time runs back upon itself, is the clasp of these stories and so it is fitting that the telling should begin and end there.

This final account of the Stone's journey to Baile na Cille comes from a pivotal age, when legend begins to rub shoulders with history and when the half-remembered stories of old men have given way to the relentless advance of the scribes and the chroniclers. Much of this story is so well documented in Scottish, English, Norwegian and Icelandic history that we can locate it precisely in the year 1290, when another young princess set out on a fateful sea voyage to Scotland. This was the tangled tale of the young Princess Margaret, on whose shoulders rested the hopes of three nations for alliance and peace. She was heir to both the Norwegian and Scottish thrones, betrothed to the English Prince Edward, son of King Edward I, and she died mysteriously in the Orkney islands on a sea voyage from Norway to Scotland:

that much is universally agreed. The circumstances of her death are obscure, however, and have given rise to many conflicting accounts and much lingering suspicion. Some believe she was kidnapped and reemerged in Germany years later, only to be burned at the stake as an imposter on the orders of King Eirik of Norway. Others say she was drowned, her body taken back to Bergen and buried there. Still others impute her death to disease, to seasickness or even poisoning. The young Margaret's untimely end cast Scotland's hopes for secure alliance with England and Norway into disarray. Further, it left the door open to the dangerous possibility of other claimants to the ancient throne of the Scottish kings. Such a consequential death cries out for certainty, but there is none. The only secure facts are that the Princess never reached Scotland, where she would have become queen, that she died in questionable circumstances and that she was accompanied on her voyage by a Norwegian woman of noble birth, Fru Ingibiorg, of whom little is known.

What part, if any, had the Stone in this? It would be tempting to believe that Margaret's death was simply a coincidence; an occasion when the legends of a drowned princess were mirrored by recorded history. And so it might be, were it not for the presence in the story of Fru Ingibiorg.

Fru Ingibiorg knew herself to be of royal ancestry, descended from the great Jarl Skule Tostesson himself. It was said that her family had been cheated of their legitimate claim to the throne of Norway by ancestors of King Eirik. It was her contention, which was hard to challenge in an age where records were incomplete and inexact, that she was the direct descendent of Ingibiorg Finnsdottir, who, two centuries earlier, had married Malcolm III, King of the Scots. Ingibiorg Finnsdottir was mother of the Scottish King Duncan II. In this way, like the Princess Margaret, Fru Ingibiorg had some claim to both the Norwegian and the Scottish thrones, although her claim was less strong. It was widely rumoured that, through her inheritance, she was now in possession of the notorious Tostesson Seeing Stone. If the Stone had been present throughout the murky circumstances of Margaret's death, it would seem certain that it must have imposed some influence on the death itself and on subsequent events.

Fru Ingibiorg was a proud woman. Like so many of the nobility whose circumstances had been reduced, she held herself in high esteem, while harbouring a well-hidden resentment of those whom she believed had usurped her royal status. She had a faction of supporters within the court who were plotting, in the event of Margaret's death, to forward her as the most worthy successor to the Princess. Outwardly Ingibiorg would give her approval to none of this. On the surface, she was contented in her station as a wise, charming and loyal companion to the young Princess Margaret. None, in the royal court, suspected that in secret she used the Stone to foresee futures that would lead to the death of her mistress. Alone in her chamber, she would open the secret pouch she wore on her neckpiece and take from it an ornate key, whose head was fashioned as an intricate Celtic knot. She would use this key to unlock a yew box, removing from it the Stone of Jarl Skule Tostesson. Ingibiorg was skilled with the Stone, perhaps second only in skill to the Brahan Seer himself. It is possible that she could not only see the future, but could use the Stone to manipulate it to her advantage.

"Conjure me her death," she whispered as she raised the Tostesson Stone to her eye.

The Stone gave her many confusing responses. Sometimes, as she squinted through its narrow aperture, she saw her young rival Margaret becoming Queen of Norway, Scotland and England, uniting the three kingdoms into a formidable empire. At other times, she herself was elevated into the royalty and became first the Princess Ingibiorg and then the queen of three realms. Gradually she learned to guide the Stone's tellings into channels that favoured her own fortunes to the detriment of Margaret. One particular sighting occurred again and again. It was of the Princess Margaret and Fru Ingibiorg undertaking a voyage together. While at sea the Princess wore Ingibiorg's neckpiece around her own slender neck. Ingibiorg sensed that the future would pivot on this moment but could not understand its significance, nor how it would alter their balance of fortunes.

Then, suddenly, everything became clear. The betrothal was announced between Margaret and Edward, son of the English King and it was agreed that the young Princess should be taken to London by way of the Orkneys. Fru Ingibiorg was selected to accompany the Princess on the journey. In the privacy of her chamber, she consulted her Stone. It showed her vivid images of their departure from Bergen, of six festooned ships leaving the harbour amid much pomp, of the two-week crossing to Kirkwall and, during it, the Princess wearing her companion's neckpiece.

"So this is what will happen," Ingibiorg mused, "this is what the Stone has been telling me."

The Stone offered her another image. It was of the Princess, lying still beneath the water, drowned and wearing the sodden neckpiece. Ingibiorg saw her body being dragged from the sea; how the neckpiece became unclasped, how hands reached for it, opened its pouch and pulled from it the Stone, a key and a ring. Immediately she recognised the ornate key to the Stone's yew box. The ring was inscribed with runes and, set into it, a small irregular red jewel, its outline resembling that of a seal. Ingibiorg stared at it with a thudding heart. She knew that very ring; she had it in her keepsake box; the last of her great grandmother's possessions. She had always disdained it as a slight and misshapen thing, knowing nothing of its history or significance, but she had never found the resolve to throw it away.

That night, in her bedchamber, Ingibiorg strove to weave the images she had seen into a meaningful pattern. At length she decided the Stone was showing her that, through the wearing of the neckpiece, the death of the Princess was assured. But, to fulfill the prophecy in all its detail, she herself would have to place the Stone, the key and the seal ring into the pouch stitched to her plaited neckpiece. This she did.

During the voyage, Fru Ingibiorg made several artful attempts to encourage Margaret to wear the neckpiece but the Princess resisted. It was not until they were into the second week of the crossing that a favourable moment arose. The seas were heavy and the young Princess was wracked by severe seasickness. Ingibiorg saw her opportunity.

"I'm protected from seasickness," she said, "because I wear this neckpiece. Here, let me put it upon you to see if it will help."

So saying, she firmly clasped the necklace on her young mistress who, by this time, had become too weak to resist.

During the days that followed she took the Princess up onto the open deck, on the pretence that fresh air would be curative. Secretly, she had visions of violent waves breaking over the deck and sweeping her young rival to her drowning but, although the water was rough, nothing untoward happened. The Princess, weak and wretched, remained ill and unable to eat and soon was confined to her cabin. Three days later they sighted the Orkney islands. Ingibiorg began to doubt the Stone's vision.

The ships anchored in the harbour at Kirkwall, where the Princess was taken ashore, deathly pale; still wearing the neckpiece. For several days her condition worsened and it became apparent that she would not recover. Still she lingered on the edge of life, her frail fingers fretting at the plaited leather and its small pouch. Then, in the chill light of an early morning, Princess Margaret of Norway died. The captains and the diplomats were thrown into the deepest consternation. There was much dispute between them as to the most appropriate disposition of the body. The girl could be buried at Kirkwall, although the Orkney islands seemed an impoverished place to lay a Princess who had been the hope of three kingdoms. Or they could return to Norway, although that option was tainted with the probability of disgrace and retribution for their negligence.

A faction of diplomats amongst the retinue saw an opportunity to advance the Lady Ingibiorg and, in so doing, to further themselves.

"She is of Norwegian royal lineage," they argued, "and is also in direct descent from the Scots King Malcolm. It is fitting, this being an affair of great consequence, that we should proceed to Scotland with the Lady Ingibiorg as Margaret's representative to bear the sad news to the Scottish Council of Guardians and to confer with them as to the appropriate actions."

The motives of these Norwegian diplomats were transparent to the ship captains, who knew too well that Fru Ingibiorg and her advisers would use this occasion to advance their own cause. Nevertheless, compared with the prospect of returning to Bergen, most felt it a preferable course and so they concurred. One captain dissented from this consensus and it was agreed that he should return to Bergen, bearing the remains of Margaret, while the others continued west to Scotland. Ingibiorg was charged with preparing the body for its sad return. She first retrieved her neckpiece, clasping it back around her own neck. *The Stone was both wrong and right,* she reflected. *Margaret died, though not of a drowning. But the nub of the prophecy was death for her and advancement for me. It is on that course that we now steer.* She dressed the Princess in her royal finery and, in this state, the body was transferred with all solemnity to the returning vessel.

When it had departed, the remaining fleet of five ships continued westward. Ingibiorg was pleased to note that the captains and diplomats treated her with a new respect. She was now the Lady Ingibiorg, even to those who had formerly refused to acknowledge her title. The common sailors took to calling her

Our New Princess, which she found immensely gratifying, although she was careful not to show it. She dressed herself in her finest clothes and held her head high, affecting a certain haughtiness with those around her. In every way she could, Ingibiorg worked to become a princess, basking in the attention of the diplomats as they consulted her as to their course of action with the Scottish Council. There was talk that she should herself proceed to London where she might represent Norway or even, if her reception by the English was propitious, lay a claim to the Norwegian or even the Scottish succession.

In her cabin Ingibiorg took the Stone from its leather pouch at her neck and sought guidance from it. It vouchsafed her a series of confused and tumbling images that made no sense. She could see only visions of sea and death. The Stone showed her another princess in a different age, with long flaxen tresses. She saw a ship held at anchor by a rope woven entirely of hair. One scene repeated itself with a frightening insistence. It was of her own plaited leather neckpiece, now sea-soaked and blackened, around the neck of a drowned princess. Each time this vision appeared, the princess had a different face, her submerged, streaming hair sometimes fair, sometimes dark and sometimes a disturbingly vivid red.

The weather worsened and, as if in sympathy with the storm, so did the Stone's visions. Now it showed a frenzied prophet, his hair aflame, who appeared screaming above the crescendo of the gale; next came images of red-haired women; women whose hair streamed like kelp, of seals and selkies, magicians and seers, all of them distorted and wild.

A huge wave crashed down upon the fleet. Sailors were thrown to the deck and there was a clap of thunder so loud that the five ships shook to their keel roots. The tempest intensified to a new and unimaginable ferocity.

Heedless now of the rain and salt spray which soaked her

fine clothes, Ingibiorg battled her way up onto the deck. Terror tugged at her, snaking her thoughts away into the sea. The waves grew into mountains. The little ships were sucked into wave troughs only to be tossed up onto the next foaming crest, where Gallan Head was now visible through the spume on the port bow. Beyond lay the sands of Uig Bay, as yet out of sight, and the twisting knot in time that was Baile na Cille. There came a sudden lull in the storm and, for an instant, the wind subsided into nothing. Frozen in place, the ship remained poised on a wave crest, the deck engulfed by stillness. In this subdued moment, time stopped. Ingibiorg stood, holding the Stone, and there was not even breeze enough to ruffle the fabric of her clothes. With a strange detachment she looked down at the sleeve of her dress and saw the minute detail of its warp and weft, how the cunning weave crossed beneath itself; disappeared and reappeared transformed. All was caught in an eternity of stillness. Ingibiorg was overcome by an inexplicable peace that descended upon her as she looked at the Stone nestled in her hand. As she raised it, its colour shifted from white to a pale blue and its runic markings appeared to melt and coalesce into new patterns. She returned the Stone to its leather pouch and a realisation came over her. This moment, or variations of this moment, had happened before and would happen again unceasingly.

In the vortex of time, here, she knew that she had made this journey before. She was indeed a princess. She was the Princess Gradhag, whose rhyming bested the Blue Men of the Minch, only to drown in this very storm. She became Halldóra, who held the Stone as she leapt to her death, weeping for her lover sucked into the whirlpool at Lochlin. She was transformed into a selkie with the Stone embedded in her collar. She would become Peggy of the red hair, securing the Stone for her son, the Brahan Seer. At last Ingibiorg saw the truth of it: that she and countless other bearers of the Stone were the individual and inseparable threads intricately woven into the fabric of time and its tale. She felt a profound reconciliation and, without use of the Stone, foresaw herself in a quiet pool, staring up with calm, sightless eyes.

The long, still moment came abruptly to an end. A huge wave, more fearsome than any yet seen, crashed down upon the fleet. The five Norwegian ships shook and their stout timbers splintered and cracked. The tempest reached a new and unimaginable ferocity. In the continuing tumult, all five ships foundered and were lost.

Their remnants were carried along by the inexorable currents that sweep across the sands of Uig Bay. Next morning the people of Uig would find the wreckage. A child from Timsgarry would come upon a woman's body lying beneath the water, staring up, her pale face unmoving and her hair wafting like kelp in the current. Around her neck on a plaited neckpiece would be a pouch containing a ring, a key and a seeing stone.

This tale would seem simple. It is of a princess drowned in the pool at Baile na Cille on the sands of Uig, where a peat-brown river frets at the edge of the sea. You would seem to know the end of the story before you know its beginning. Yet, like a Celtic knot, when its intricacies are traced there is no beginning, only twists and retellings that loop without ending.

Endnotes

1 The Seer, in this Chapter, is named *Kenneth Odhar*. Throughout this book, he will be called by other names as he was in life. Each of these names, such as *Kenneth of Seaforth* or *Coinneach MacKenzie*, is taken from the source material that provided the basis for that particular version of the tale. The exception, *Kennie the Wind* in Chapter 11, is my own invention.

2 This Seeing Stone of Lochlin is variously called the Lochlann Stone, the Stone of the Seer and the Brahan Stone. In many accounts it is simply *the Stone*. Moreover it is sometimes described as white, sometimes blue and sometimes pale. Even its shape is a matter of contention, giving rise to possibilities that there may have existed more than one Stone, that the Stone changed shape and hue in different strands of time, or that a tale's detail is ever at the mercy of the teller. Although accounts differ as to the shape and colour of the Stone, or whether runes could be seen upon its surface, there is general agreement that the Stone always fitted the hand with a seductive precision, as if formed for the purpose.

3 St Kilda was called 'The High Country' and sailors spoke of the Flannan Isles as 'The Land of Fowling', both namings arising from a fear that drowning, or other dire consequence, would surely come to any who spoke the true names before setting forth to those distant islands.

4 In other versions the Stone is white or pale.

5 In yet another version told in Uig, the princess is from Norway. A seer, whose name is unknown, is ordered by the Norse king to use his Stone to foresee the consequences of a reprisal raid on Lewis for failure to pay tributes and taxes. The seer is reluctant but the King presses him. He foretells tragedy and shipwreck for the expedition, whereupon the King is enraged and attacks him

207

with a spear. The Norse princess intervenes to rescue the seer, who gives her his stone in gratitude. She dresses as a boy and joins the raid, thinking that the stone will protect her but is drowned with her comrades off Uig sands.

6   Birka of Björkö appears in several versions of the tale. In each he is a seer – sometimes blind, sometimes sighted. In each, his *seeing* has unfortunate consequences for him which involve blindness or injury and, ultimately, he always brings misfortune to the House of Lochlin.

7   Mr. Kenneth Sinclair, a farmer living at Loch Ussie, believes the Stone to be there to this day and that "it will be found by a man with two thumbs on the one hand".

8   A monument to a similar happening can be seen still, called the *Clach-a-mharslin*, being the Rock of the Pedlar, lying to the west of the village of Kinloch Rannoch.

9   In other versions of the tale she is Margaret Crowther or, sometimes, Crowder.

10 For the fate of Rab Robertson and the fulfilment of the Seer's prophecy concerning his wealth, see *On the Nature of the Blue Men of the Minch*

11 The giant Blue Man in this telling is said by some to be the father of the giant of Uig, named *Chuithaich*, who is buried in a broch by the shores of Uig Bay. The giant was eleven feet high and oppressed the people of Uig before being defeated in combat by Fionn and the Feinne.

12 The meat of cormorants is nourishing; the oil is good and is the best cure for whooping cough. The dried birds, feathers and all, make fine torches that will not blow out on a windy night.

13 Otherwise known as the White Men, the Merry Dancers or the *Aurora Borealis*

14 Silver is the metal of protection, being resistant to enchantment and a sure remedy against all poisons.

15 In some versions of this tale, Godwinson puts the Stone to his eye and sees a profitable cargo of walrus ivory. In this way, the Stone is active in initiating its tortuous journey from Trondheim to Skye.

16 The first recorded use of bishops in chess is in the Icelandic sagas, some fifty years before the bishop was substituted for the *Alfil* or elephant that was universally found in early medieval chess sets across Europe. This has been used by some to argue that the famed Lewis Chessmen originated in Iceland, not in Trondheim as has been generally supposed.

17 Some think that in disregarding the Stone, Godwinson committed a slight that the Stone would later punish by giving erroneous information that led to the death of Godwinson, his crew and the loss of his treasure.

18 A Lewisman named Malcolm MacLeod is reputed to have been the finder of the Lewis Chessmen in the vicinity of Uig some centuries later. This has led some to suppose that it is the same person. The evidence for this would be slender, were it not for the Seer's prophecy that a one-eyed MacLeod would discover a great treasure hidden on Tanera Mor.

19 It would be characteristic of the Seer's foretellings, particularly those emanating from use of the Stone, that they are rarely straightforward. To this day, local people aver that a MacLeod is yet to possess the legendary treasure of Tanera Mor, not apprehending that the prophecy has long been completed; a one-eyed MacLeod did indeed discover the treasure although he did not take it.

20 Some have suggested that Godwinson's bold actions, being so unlike his normal cautious behaviour, indicate that he must have used the Stone to foresee these events and to be prepared in advance for the riddling. However, it is more likely that he never consulted the Stone but relied solely on his memory of the Saga stanza.

21 Huw Edwardes-Evans has provided this interpretation of the first stanza of chapter 60 from *Egil's Saga*, which is used here with gratitude.

22 This prediction is questionable. Despite continuing legend and rumour among Lewismen about the Black Nuns, no convent has ever been shown to exist at Mealista or elsewhere in the immediate neighbourhood of Uig. However, there had long been established a settlement, *Tigh nan Cailleachan Dubha*, or The House of the Black Women, which can also be translated as 'Black Nuns', in that area. Black was the common dress of widows and, indeed, of the majority of older women. This was a community where widowed or impoverished women gathered together. They would certainly not have possessed the collective means to purchase even a single pawn. This raises several possibilities. Perhaps the Stone or the Seer lied. Perhaps the Black Nuns of Mealista existed but upon a different thread of time.

23 Tomnahurich, the Hill of Yews, was a place of danger and enchantment. Fairies lived there and, to satisfy their love of music, they would entrap passing fiddlers and take them deep within the Hill. Any fiddler unfortunate enough to fall into the fairies' clutches would be imprisoned for one hundred years and forced to play at the captors' whim. After exactly one hundred years, the fiddler, dazed and tottering, would be ejected at the side of the hill, not one day older than when captured.

24 There are grassed-over remains of several burnt mounds still
   visible at Brahan around Loch Ussie. They date from the earliest
   times and their original purpose is obscure; probably connected
   with communal food preparation. Stone troughs have often been
   found at the sites of burnt mounds, leading to the supposition that
   the mounds also had some ritualistic purpose. Local people living
   near one of these mounds at Loch Ussie insist that the Brahan Seer
   hid there for several days prior to his capture and execution.

25 Thus, the Stone in Loch Ussie crossed a thread of time and, by
   a set of curious chances, came into the hands of young Kenneth
   Odhar, *a Seer as great as himself.*

On the Nature of the Team Behind the Book

Neil Rackham, Author

Neil is best known as an author of business books, including the global sales classic, *SPIN® Selling.* He lives in the usa but is a frequent visitor to Britain, having visiting professorships at Sheffield and Edinburgh Napier Universities. Seeking solitude and opportunities to walk took Neil to Scotland, the land of his forebears. He spent time in the Outer Hebrides, staying at the holiday home of his childhood friend Catriona Nicholson (née MacSween) and it was there that the genesis for this book was shaped. As the manuscript progressed it became clear that it would be much enhanced by illustrations and so he approached Alisdair Wiseman, who draws stones like nobody else. It transpired that Neil and Alisdair had business interests in common and thus a happy collaboration was born.

Alisdair Wiseman, Illustrator

Alisdair has dreamt of illustrating a book since poring over Arthur Rackham's glorious illustrations in *Rip Van Winkle* as a teenager. Imagine his surprise when he was invited to illustrate a book written by Neil Rackham, a descendent of Arthur, and then when he discovered that Neil was the author of *SPIN® Selling*, the sales process that Alisdair has used for many years in his 'proper' job as a facilitator with The Innovation Zone. Clearly, greater forces were at work here! When not travelling the world spreading the word on innovation, Alisdair helps his wife Les to run their gallery in the Outer Hebrides. He also tries, without success, to get to the end of his to-do list. Alisdair works primarily in watercolour but his original passion is illustrating in pen and ink.

Emily Benton, Designer
Emily is a freelance book designer. emilybentonbookdesigner.co.uk
She studied for her ma in 2014 in the department of typography at
Reading University. She has since produced publications for John
Morgan studio, artists Antony Gormley and Ragnar Kjartansson, as
well as for many art galleries including the Barbican, the Sainsbury
Centre, Raven Row and The Artist's Institute in New York. Emily has
a strong interest in sustainability and a passion for climbing rocks.
When not designing books she can be found in old bookshops, or
at her studio, fondling her collection of paper samples. She doesn't
have a favourite typeface.

Lynda Edwardes-Evans, Editor
Lynda Edwardes-Evans worked in book publishing before moving
into primary education, where she runs writing groups for children
and teachers. As a freelance book editor Lynda works closely with
authors to encourage and develop their ideas. This book is her first
encounter with the wonders of the Western Isles.

Catriona Nicholson, Co-ordinator
After a career in teaching, Catriona was a lecturer in English
and Education at Reading University. Her father's family come
from the Isle of Lewis and she has a holiday home on its remote
and mountainous west coast. Neil spent several summers there
in splendid isolation, reading local stories and writing his own.
Much of this book was written in that stone cottage which stands
along a road to nowhere, not very far from Baile na Cille, where
'a peat-brown river frets at the edge of the sea'.

Acknowledgements

I'm indebted to the many sources I consulted to enrich the content of this book, from snippets on the Internet to detailed and dusty books in reference libraries. Some like the excellent Martin Martin's *A Description of the Western Islands of Scotland* and Robert Heron's *The Summer Walkers* have been directly quoted, but other valuable sources of reference do stand out, starting with Dave Roberts' columns in *Uig News An t-Ùigeach* that first alerted me to the links between the Brahan Seer, the Stone and a drowned princess. Elizabeth Sutherland's books, *The Seer of Kintail* and *Ravens and Black Rain* provided me with invaluable background. I was greatly influenced by D. D. C. Pochin Mould's *West-Over-Sea* published by Acair. This remarkable account of life in the Western Isles pervades almost every chapter of my text.

Among the reference books I referred to over and over were James MacKillop's *Dictionary of Celtic Mythology*, Philip Freeman's *Celtic Mythology*, F. Marian McNeill's *The Silver Bough: Scottish Folklore and Folk-Belief*, Ian Crofton's *A Dictionary of Scottish Phrase and Fable*, Margaret Bennett's *Scottish Customs: From the Cradle to the Grave* and Peter Berresford Ellis's *Celtic Myths and Legends*.

213

ACKNOWLEDGEMENTS

The Brahan Seer has been the subject of many books, stories and articles although the two books that stand out are Alexander Mackenzie's *The Prophecies of the Brahan Seer*, originally published in 1877, and Alex Sutherland's *The Brahan Seer: the Making of a Legend*.

The deepest acknowledgements, however, must go to the anonymous storytellers who passed these legends on to successive generations, filling their long winter nights with enchantment and wonder.

NR